Language Arts 806
Language and Literature

LIFEPAC Test is located in the center of the booklet. Please remove before starting the unit.

Author:
Judith Niven

Editor-in-Chief:
Richard W. Wheeler, M.A.Ed.
Editors:
Mary Ellen Quint, M.A.
Helen Robertson Prewitt, M.A.Ed.
Consulting Editor:
Larry Howard, Ed.D.
Revision Editor:
Alan Christopherson, M.S.

Westover Studios Design Team:
Phillip Pettet, Creative Lead
Teresa Davis, DTP Lead
Nick Castro
Andi Graham
Jerry Wingo
Lauren Faulk

Alpha Omega
PUBLICATIONS

804 N. 2nd Ave. E.
Rock Rapids, IA 51246-1759

Language and Literature

Introduction

Many students are unaware of the interesting history of our language. Modern English is the product of many languages and cultures. In this LIFEPAC® you will study about the changes in the English language. As you examine the development and characteristics of Old English and Middle English, you will become familiar with some of the literature produced by the Anglo-Saxons and the writers of Medieval England.

In the second section you will learn more about Modern English usage by studying coordination and subordination.

In the third section you will read two accounts from real life. One autobiographical selection describes a small country school. The other account describes Admiral Byrd's expedition to the South Pole.

Objectives

Read these objectives. The objectives tell you what you will be able to do when you have successfully completed this LIFEPAC. When you have finished this LIFEPAC, you should be able to:

1. Briefly explain the history of Old English.

2. Explain some of the differences between Old English and Middle English.

3. List some contributions to literature made by the Anglo-Saxons.

4. Identify and use correctly coordinate conjunctions, correlative conjunctions, and conjunctive adverbs.

5. Subordinate a lesser idea to a main idea by using an adverb clause, an adjective clause, a phrase, or an appositive.

6. Describe the characteristics of autobiography.

7. Identify basic elements usually included in an autobiography.

8. Spell correctly some vocabulary words and some words with similar endings.

Survey the LIFEPAC. Ask yourself some questions about this study and write your questions here.

_____
_____
_____
_____
_____
_____
_____
_____
_____
_____
_____
_____
_____
_____
_____
_____
_____
_____
_____
_____
_____
_____

1. THE NATURE OF LANGUAGE

Hwaet rece we hwaet we sprecan…. Greek? Latin? Certainly it is an unknown language. Surprisingly enough, it is English, but this form of English is the forerunner of the language you speak and write daily. In this section you will examine the history and characteristics of the Old English and Middle English language. You will also look at some examples from both periods that will enable you to understand the impact history has had on *written* language.

SECTION OBJECTIVES

Review these objectives. When you have completed this section, you should be able to:
1. Briefly explain the history of Old English.
2. Explain some of the differences between Old English and Middle English.
3. List some contributions to literature made by the Anglo-Saxons.

VOCABULARY

Study these words to enhance your learning success in this section.

alliterative (u lit′ u rā tiv). Lines of verse having words beginning with the same initial sounds.
dialect (dī′ u lekt). The local characteristics of speech that deviate from a real or imaginary standard speech.
epic (ep′ ik). A long narrative poem about the deeds of a hero.
inflection (in flek′ shun). The change of form in words to indicate grammatical relationships such as number, case, gender, and so forth.

Note: *All vocabulary words in this LIFEPAC appear in* **boldface** *print the first time they are used. If you are not sure of the meaning when you are reading, study the definitions given.*

Pronunciation Key: hat, āge, cãre, fär; let, ēqual, tėrm; it, īce; hot, ōpen, ôrder; oil; out; cup, pu̇t, rüle; child; long; thin; /ŦH/ for then; /zh/ for measure; /u/ represents /a/ in about, /e/ in taken, /i/ in pencil, /o/ in lemon, and /u/ in circus.

OLD ENGLISH

The roots of English language and literature are found in the period of history known as the Anglo-Saxon, or Old English period. The Anglo-Saxon period dates from about A.D. 449 to A.D. 1066.

Old English history. Before the year 449, Britain had been occupied by the Celts and the Romans. The Celts were a warlike tribe that inhabited an area that extended from Ireland to Britain, to the continent (modern France, Germany, Spain, and Switzerland), to the Balkans, and to Asia Minor. The Celts spoke their own unique language. Some forms of this language still remain in Ireland, Wales, and Brittany. The Celts in Britain were called Britons.

The Romans began to invade Britain in 55 B.C. because they wanted the resources, tin and wool, that the island could provide. The Romans remained in Britain until A.D. 449, when they took their troops out of Britain to defend Rome.

After the Romans left, the Britons had few defenses against their enemies. The Britain king, Vortigern, asked the Angles and the Saxons to help him defeat his Celtic enemies, the Picts and the Scots. What Vortigern did not realize, however, was that the Angles and the Saxons did not intend to leave Britain once they had helped him. These Anglo-Saxons went on to fight the Britons, whom they had come to help.

The Britons fled to the western hills, or were defeated.

By the sixth century Britain was almost completely occupied by the invading Germanic tribes, who began to establish small kingdoms. The names of these kingdoms reflected the names of the invader. Wessex was settled by West Saxon. Essex was settled by the East Saxons. East Anglia was settled by the East Angles, and so forth.

The culture, the traditions, and the language of these small tribes reflected a combination of the Germanic and the Latin-Roman influences as well as some Celtic remnants. The Christian church also influenced culture, tradition, and language. Monasteries had been established by the seventh century in both the North and the Southeast.

These monasteries became centers of learning and culture. Monks were sought as teachers by other countries. Charlemagne came to English monasteries to find teachers for his palace schools.

Between the sixth and the eighth centuries these early Germanic invaders established themselves in England. Together with those Britons and Romans who remained, they became the English nation. The Venerable Bede, a monk who was England's greatest scholar in the seventh and eighth centuries, wrote down the history of this early period in *The Ecclesiastical History of the English Nation*.

This period between the sixth and eighth centuries was also a period of relative peace. Many of the poems that survived were probably composed at this time, even though the surviving manuscripts are from later times.

Late in the eighth century, Danish Vikings began to invade Britain. They raided monasteries and churches, destroying artifacts and manuscripts. These invasions continued for almost a century until Alfred, king of Wessex, finally stopped them and restricted these invaders to one section of land known as the Danelaw.

King Alfred, also called Alfred the Great, was a soldier and a scholar. After he had defeated the Danes, Alfred worked to restore England to the level of culture and education that it had know before the Danish invasions began. Alfred set up new schools and had many works translated from Latin and Greek into Anglo-Saxon so that the people could learn to hear these works in a familiar language.

After Alfred died, Wessex continued to be a center of learning. Alfred's heirs eventually won back the Danelaw and England became a united country. In 1017, a Danish king, Cnut captured England and made it part of his Danish kingdom.

In 1042 an English king, Edward the Confessor, once again ruled. His reign lasted until his death in 1066. After Edward's death, two men tried to claim the English throne, one from Wessex, and one from Normandy. In 1066 William of Normandy won the struggle in what is called the Norman Conquest. This date marks the end of Anglo-Saxon England. From this point in history, the Normans influenced culture, tradition, and language.

Match these items.

1.1	_____ Celts	a.	Monk
1.2	_____ Romans	b.	Danish king
1.3	_____ Bede	c.	Latin king
1.4	_____ Vortigern	d.	Britons
1.5	_____ Cnut	e.	55 B.C. - A.D. 449
		f.	Briton king

Answer true or false.

1.6 _____ The Anglo-Saxons were Germanic.

1.7 _____ The Christian church had no influence.

1.8 _____ The Danish Vikings invaded England in the late eighth century.

1.9 _____ The Danelaw was a king.

1.10 _____ Alfred the Great defeated the Danes.

1.11 _____ Edward the Confessor led the Norman Conquest.

1.12 _____ The Norman Conquest in 1066 ended the Anglo-Saxon period.

Old English language. In Anglo-Saxon England, the language spoken was basically a Germanic language that had been influenced by Latin. This language also had **dialects**, each slightly different from the others. The four main dialects of Anglo-Saxon are called Northumbrian, Mercian, West Saxon, and Kentish. If Anglo-Saxon had remained untouched by the Norman Conquest, the language known as English today would be very different.

Anglo-Saxon was an **inflected** language. It did not depend on word order in the way that Modern English does.

The best way to understand the differences between Anglo-Saxon and Modern English is to look at some examples of each language.

Some words have changed very little or not at all since the Anglo-Saxon period. Many pronouns, for example, are nearly the same today as they were a thousand years ago. Study the following pronoun charts and notice the similarities and the differences between these two languages. (The "þ" was pronounced "th.")

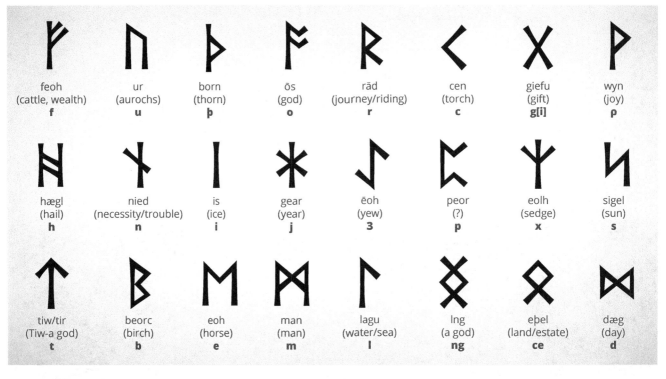

| Anglo-Saxon Runic Alphabet

Anglo-Saxon Pronouns				
	first person	**second person**	**third person**	
singular	ic	þū	hē	hit	hēo
	min	þ īn	his	his	hiere
	mē	þē	him	him	hire
	mē	þē	hine	hit	hie
plural	wē	gē	hīe		
	ūre	ēower	hiere		
	ūs	ēow	him		
	ūs	ēow	hīe		

Modern English Pronouns				
	first person	**second person**	**third person**	
singular	I	you, thou	he	it	she
	mine or my	yours, thine, or thy	his	its	hers
	me	thee	him		her
plural	we	you or ye	they		
	our	your	theirs		
	us		them		

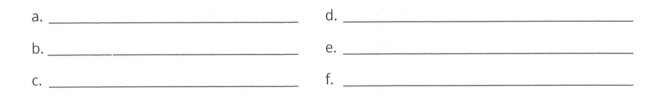

Complete this activity.

1.13 Find the pronouns that have remained the same and list them.

a. _____   d. _____

b. _____   e. _____

c. _____   f. _____

Before looking at more Anglo-Saxon words, the Anglo-Saxon vowel sounds must be studied. The vowel sounds are slightly different and include at least two vowels, "y" and "æ" that Modern English no longer uses.

The "y" had a sound like a German "ü." The "æ" had a sound like the "a" in *hat*.

Anglo-Saxon Vowels			
a	as in hot	ī	as in teen
ā	as in father	o	as in audio
æ	as in cat	ō	as in wrote
æ	as in dad	u	as in full
e	as in bet	ū	as in room
ē	as in late	y	as in German ü
i	as in hit	ȳ	as in German ü

Some consonant sounds also differ from Modern English.

Anglo-Saxon Consonants	
c̄	as in chalk
c	as in card
cg	as "dg" in ridge
f	as in father (in the beginning of a word)
f	as in over (between two vowels)
ġ	as in yes
g	as in get
h	as in heart (in the beginning of a word)
h	as in German "ch"
sc	as in ship
þ	as in thin
ð	as in them

 Complete these activities.

1.14   Study the pronunciation charts and try pronouncing these words with a friend.

a. fæder   e. mōdor   i. hwā

b. dohtor   f. mann   j. hwǽr

c. dæġ   g. eorþan   k. scēap

d. bæc   h. pĕer   l. scip

1.15   Now try to translate the words in 1.14 into Modern English.
Work with a helper if you have difficulty.

a. _____   b. _____

c. _____   d. _____

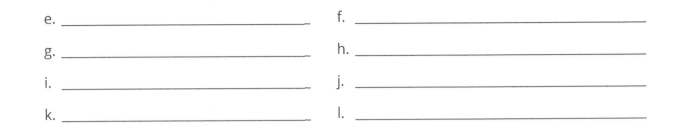

e. _____   f. _____

g. _____   h. _____

i. _____   j. _____

k. _____   l. _____

Write the letter of the correct answer.

1.16   Anglo-Saxon was a _____ language.
　　　a. Germanic　　　b. Spanish　　　c. Greek

1.17   Anglo-Saxon was a/an _____ language.
　　　a. fragmented　　　b. inflected　　　c. simple

1.18   The main Anglo-Saxon dialects were Kentish, Northumbrian, _____ .
　　　a. Latin, and German　　　　　　b. French, and Latin
　　　c. Mercian, and West Saxon

1.19   The Anglo-Saxon pronoun for *it* was _____ .
　　　a. *ic*　　　b. *hit*　　　c. *hiere*

1.20   The Anglo-Saxon word for mother is _____ .
　　　a. mother　　　b. mōdor　　　c. mæder

Once the vowels and consonant differences are understood, reading some Anglo-Saxon no longer seems so difficult. The following two examples are taken from things that are often read and heard.

Faeder ūre, þū þe eart on heofonum, si þin nama gehālgod. Tobecume þin rīce. Gewurþe ðin willa on eorþan swā swā on heofonum. Ūrne gedaeghwām-lican hlāf syle ūs tō daeg. And forgyf ūs ūre gyltas, swā swā wē forgyfaðūrum gyltendum. And ne gelæd þū ūs on costnunge, ac ālys ūs of yfele. So þlice.

Gospel excerpt (Mark 4:4–8)

(4) And þā hē sēow, sum fēoll wið þone weg, and fugelas cōmon and hit fræton. (5) Sum fēoll ofer stānscyligean, þār hit næfde mycele eorðan, and sōna ūp ēode; and for ðām hit naede eorðan þiccnesse, (6) þā hit ūp ēode, sēo sunne hit forswælde, and hit forscranc, for þām hit wyrtruman næfde. (7) And sum fēoll on þornas; þā stigon ðā pornas and forðrysmodon þæt, and hit wæstm ne bær. (8) And sum fēoll on gōd land, and hit sealde ūppstīgendne and wexendne wæstm; and ān brōhte prītigfealdne, sum syxtigfealdne, sum hundfealdne.

Complete these activities.

1.21 Try reading the two preceding passages aloud. You should recognize the first one immediately.

It is _____ . Compare it to Matthew 6:9b–13.

1.22 The second passage is from Mark chapter 4. Locate the verses.

They are verses _____ . Compare these verses to the preceding passage.

1.23 From the first passage list the words that you recognized easily.
Write the modern English spelling. List each word only *once*.

_____   _____

_____   _____

_____   _____

_____   _____

_____   _____

_____   _____

_____   _____

_____   _____

_____

1.24 List at least five words from Mark chapter 4 that you recognize easily.
Write the modern English spelling.

_____

_____

_____

_____

_____

_____

_____

_____

Old English literature. Scholars can only estimate the amount and kinds of Anglo-Saxon literature that has been written. Because of time, wars, and a scarcity of written manuscripts, only a small body of Anglo-Saxon literature survived. The poems, sermons, riddles, charms, and gnomic verses that did survive are preserved in manuscripts copied by monks many years after these works were actually written.

Some manuscripts and artifacts of this period are still being discovered by scholars and archaeologists. One such find at Sutton Hoo, in 1939, uncovered an Anglo-Saxon ship-burial dating back to the mid-seventh century. The dishes, helmets, swords, jewelry, and the religious articles found at Sutton Hoo fit the descriptions of such artifacts in many Anglo-Saxon poems, especially in *Beowulf*. Archaeology, more than any other discipline in this century, has helped scholars and others interested in the Anglo-Saxons to understand that the Anglo-Saxons had a refined, intelligent culture. This culture was unlike that of other countries at the time and was destroyed ultimately by the Norman Conquest.

The Anglo-Saxon literature that did survive proves that these people were creative poets and storytellers. Many of the Anglo-Saxon poems are elegies, or poems written about such serious subjects as the shortness of life and the certainty of death.

The reasons for this emphasis on the shortness of life were the harsh living conditions and the threat of war endured by even the wealthiest men. The weather was cold and damp, especially in the winter. Sickness and Viking raids were a constant threat. Under such conditions, these people became very much aware of suffering and death. To make life a little easier, men banded together in groups under a leader. The leader would take care of the men and their families, if the men would promise to help their leader in time of war. This group of men and their leader was called the *comitatus*. To live outside the *comitatus* was very lonely and dangerous.

Most Anglo-Saxon poetry was probably composed between the sixth and eighth centuries. Most of the authors are unknown. These poems survive, however, only in manuscripts written down about the year 1000.

Anglo-Saxon prose and a few Anglo-Saxon poems were written between the time of Alfred the Great (849-899) and the Norman Conquest (1066). These works often can be traced to a specific author.

The oldest Anglo-Saxon poem is probably "Widsith," a poem about a wandering *scop*, or poet, who tells of great men and of places far away. Widsith is searching for a new leader.

Other Anglo-Saxon elegies also talk about men whose leaders have died and who are now searching for a new *comitatus*. One such poem is "The Wanderer." It tells of an "eardstapa" (earth-stepper) whose leader has died. This man is now forced to wander from one group to another seeking a new leader. His loneliness and his search lead him to think about the passing nature of all things on earth. The wanderer, however, finally finds his strength in God.

"The Seafarer," a poem about a seaman, also shows an older man thinking back on the life he once had at sea.

"The Ruin" is a poem about an ancient city. It, too, asks questions about the short life of worldly things.

The Anglo-Saxons wrote many sermons and religious works. Since the church and the monastic schools were the centers of learning, religious themes were absorbed into the literature. Anglo-Saxon translations of the Bible in both prose and poetry exist today.

Riddles, charms, and wise sayings (*gnomes*) were also part of Anglo-Saxon literature. The riddles were very cleverly written. In each riddle an object, an animal, or an element of nature would describe itself and then, ask, "What am I?"

The most famous Anglo-Saxon poem is the **epic** *Beowulf*. *Beowulf* is a very long poem that tells the story of a brave hero, Beowulf, and two important battles in his life. The first battle takes place when Beowulf is still a young noble. He and his men go to help a Danish king, Hrothgar, whose kingdom is being stalked by a man-eating monster named Grendel. Beowulf defeats Grendel in a hand-to-hand fight. Soon after this victory Beowulf defeats Grendel's mother who had attacked the king's men in order to avenge Grendel's death.

The second fight takes place about fifty years after the first one. Beowulf, a king himself, has to fight a fire-breathing dragon that is attacking his kingdom. Beowulf knows that this battle with the dragon will mean death, but he goes out in spite of this knowledge to save his people.

The Anglo-Saxon period holds a rich heritage for all English speaking people. This period is beginning to be recognized as an important historical period because of recent discoveries that prove the richness of its culture.

Match these items.

1.25	_____	*Beowulf*	a.	riddle
1.26	_____	*comitatus*	b.	elegy
1.27	_____	"Wanderer"	c.	epic
1.28	_____	Sutton Hoo	d.	wise-saying
1.29	_____	gnomes	e.	leader and men
			f.	ship-burial

Complete these projects.

1.30 In your library, online, or in an encyclopedia look up Sutton Hoo. Read about it.
Write a one-page paper about what you have learned. Share your paper with the class.

TEACHER CHECK _____ _____
initials   date

1.31 Read a translation of one of the following list of Anglo-Saxon works.
Write a few paragraphs describing your reaction to your reading.

Beowulf   Anglo-Saxon Riddles

"The Seafarer"   "The Wanderer"

TEACHER CHECK _____ _____
initials   date

MIDDLE ENGLISH

After the Norman Conquest the Anglo-Saxon culture and language began to decline. The Normans were French. Their language was Old French mixed with the Germanic language of the first Normans who had been Danish Vikings.

Anglo-Saxon continued to be spoken by the common people, but it was influenced by the languages of French and Latin used by their conquerors.

Middle English history. The Middle English period (1066-1500) saw many power struggles between kings of French descent and those of English descent. Society was changing from a system of servants and lords to a system of trade in the cities. A growing middle class influenced culture, language, and customs. The days of "Lords and Ladies" lasted into the thirteenth century and even beyond, but life was more elegant in stories than in reality.

The Crusades influenced society and cultures as well. Although the Crusades were supposed to be religious wars waged to save the Holy Land, they failed miserably from the military point of view. What the Crusades did do, however, was to make England and all of Europe aware of each other and of a world quite different from their own. That world, the world of the Muslims, opened the eyes of the Crusaders to a new culture, to new artistic styles, and to new literary forms. This awareness led to the establishment of trade routes between East and West.

The growth of trade led to the growth of cities, especially cities on main trade routes or in important ports. The growth of cities meant a shift of population from the country to the city. This move changed many things, including the way men looked at themselves and at the world around them.

✏️ **Complete these sentences.**

1.32　The Normans were _____ .

1.33　Anglo-Saxon continued to be spoken by _____ .

1.34　From the military point of view, the Crusades were a _____ .

1.35　The town population a. _____ and the country population b. _____
　　　　after the Crusades.

Middle English language. The English language underwent several changes before it emerged as Modern English in the seventeenth century. The Norman Conquest brought changes primarily in vocabulary. Norman-French and Latin became the *official* languages, that is, the languages used in government and by the upper classes. New words concerned with government, with entertainment, with arts, and with learning entered the language. Vowel sounds began to change gradually. Some inflections were dropped. Changes occurred mainly in additions of new words to the language rather than in structural changes.

Several dialects grew out of Middle English. These dialects differed greatly from each other, depending on the amount of French influence in the area. Gradually the London dialect took precedence and evolved into Modern English. Study the charts of the Middle English long vowel sounds and the Middle English consonants.

Middle English Long Vowel Sounds		
Middle English Sound	**Middle English Spelling**	**Modern Pronunciation**
a	a, aa	as in f<u>a</u>ther
e, open	e, ee	as in w<u>ea</u>r
e, close	e, ee	as in pl<u>a</u>te
i	i, y	as in m<u>ee</u>t
o, open	o, oo	as in p<u>a</u>w
o, close	o, oo	as in h<u>o</u>ly
u	ou, ow, ouh	as in h<u>oo</u>t
u	u	as in f<u>ew</u>

Middle English Consonants	
Consonant	**Sound**
gg	as in dod<u>ge</u>
gg	as in da<u>gg</u>er
gh	as in <u>church</u>
gn	as g and <u>n</u>
kn, (cn)	as <u>k</u> and <u>n</u>
lf, lk, lm	as <u>l</u>
wr	as <u>w</u> and <u>r</u>

The short vowel sounds of Middle English are similar to those of Modern English. A final *e* is not silent, however, in Middle English. This final *e* is called a neutral vowel sound and is pronounced like the *a* in sofa.

Although most consonants of Middle English are pronounced as their modern counterparts, some unusual pronunciations should be noted. The chart contains these unusual consonants.

The only silent consonants, such as *h* and *gn*, appeared in words of French origin. These *h* and *gn* sounds were pronounced in Old English words. The symbols "ð" and "þ" were gradually replaced by "th."

 Complete this activity.

1.36 Read this Middle English test aloud. Use the charts if you have difficulty sounding out a word. List the words that you recognize. Write them using Modern English spelling.

A Knyght ther was, and that a worthy man,

That fro the tyme that he first bigan

To riden out, he loved chivalrie,

Trouthe and honour, fredom and curtesie.

_____

_____

_____

_____

_____

1.37 List at least three spelling differences that you notice between Middle English and Modern English.

a. _____

_____

b. _____

_____

c. _____

_____

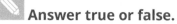 **Answer true or false.**

1.38 _____ The Western dialect became Modern English.

1.39 _____ English was the *official* language in the Middle English period.

1.40 _____ Middle English dialects differed greatly.

1.41 _____ Middle English short vowels were much the same as Modern English.

1.42 _____ Many French words came into English after 1066.

Middle English literature. Writers of the Middle English period created many types of literature. In the early centuries after 1066, most of the literature was religious or didactic; that is, it included mainly sermons, lessons, stories with a moral, or literature that taught a lesson. English literature having the quality of style and refinement of the Anglo-Saxon period did not reappear until the thirteenth and fourteenth centuries.

By the mid-fourteenth century, English literature was flourishing once again. Many forms were tried—types of romances and plays brought in from France, **alliterative** verse that renewed the Anglo-Saxon verse forms, plays, fables, and so on. The greatest writer of this time was Geoffrey Chaucer (1340-1400). Chaucer, the son of a middle class merchant, spent most of his time in London. In his lifetime Chaucer was a soldier, a valet for a noble, an ambassador, a supervisor over wool exports, a justice of the peace, a member of Parliament, and a deputy forester.

The work that Chaucer is most famous for is the *Canterbury Tales*. This long poem consists of twenty-four tales told by a group of pilgrims on their way to visit the shrine of Thomas à Becket, the archbishop who had been murdered in his cathedral in 1170. These medieval pilgrims each told tales on their way to and from the long pilgrimage to make the time pass more quickly. Chaucer not only tells a story about the pilgrimage, but also relates something about each pilgrim.

Chaucer and other poets of his time helped to establish English as the language of Britain. The invention of the printing press further helped to make the English language a uniform dialect.

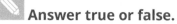 **Write the letter of the correct answer.**

1.43 Middle English literature flourished in the _____ century.
a. ninth   b. fourteenth   c. tenth

1.44 The most famous Middle English writer was _____ .
a. Chaucer   b. Alfred   c. Beowulf

1.45 The pilgrims of the Canterbury Tales went to the shrine of _____ .
a. Thomas à Becket   b. Chaucer   c. Hrothgar

Complete this project.

1.46 Read more about Chaucer. Write a 250-word essay about him. Make sure to cite your sources. Hand it in to your teacher for evaluation.

TEACHER CHECK _____ _____

initials   date

SPELLING

The words in this spelling lesson can cause confusion because of their endings. Pay special attention to these words ending with *-ance, -ence, and -ense.*

Spelling Words-1			
acceptance	attendance	nonsense	immense
intelligence	condolence	conference	grievance
remembrance	expense	existence	interference
defense	condense	experience	occurrence
alliance	intense	perseverance	superintendence
repentance	resemblance	resistance	vengeance
vigilance			

 Complete these spelling activities.

1.47 Write the root word of each *-ance* word. Use the dictionary if necessary.

a. _____ b. _____

c. _____ d. _____

e. _____ f. _____

g. _____ h. _____

i. _____ j. _____

k. _____

1.48   Use each -*ense* word in a sentence.

a. defense _____

b. expense _____

c. condense _____

d. intense _____

e. nonsense _____

f. immense _____

1.49   Arrange the -*ence* words in alphabetical order.

a. _____   b. _____

c. _____   d. _____

e. _____   f. _____

g. _____   h. _____

ABC **Ask your teacher to give you a practice spelling test of Spelling Words-1.** Restudy the words you missed.

Review the material in this section in preparation for the Self Test. The Self Test will check your mastery of this particular section. The items missed on this Self Test will indicate specific areas where restudy is needed for mastery.

SELF TEST 1

Answer true or false (each answer, 1 point).

1.01 _____ Mercian is an Anglo-Saxon dialect.

1.02 _____ Beowulf was a monk.

1.03 _____ Sutton Hoo was a Danish king.

1.04 _____ An elegy is a serious poem.

1.05 _____ Vortigern invited the Anglo-Saxons to England.

1.06 _____ The Norman Conquest brought the end of the Anglo-Saxon time.

1.07 _____ Cnut was an Anglo-Norman king.

1.08 _____ Bede wrote a history of the English people.

1.09 _____ "Widseth" was a Modern English poem.

1.010 _____ The "Wanderer" was a seaman.

Match these items (each answer, 2 points).

1.011	_____ Beowulf	a.	Norman Conquest
1.012	_____ Chaucer	b.	epic
1.013	_____ "Seafarer"	c.	Britons
1.014	_____ 1066	d.	*Canterbury Tales*
1.015	_____ Alfred	e.	55 B.C.–A.D. 449
1.016	_____ Bede	f.	elegy
1.017	_____ Celts	g.	eorðan
1.018	_____ Romans	h.	Norman king
1.019	_____ father	i.	monk
1.020	_____ earth	j.	fæder
		k.	Anglo-Saxon king

Write the modern English word (each answer, 2 points).

1.021 dæg _____

1.022 mann _____

1.023 hwær _____

1.024 scip _____

1.025 pær _____

1.026 knyght _____

1.027 hit _____

1.028 heofonum _____

1.029 trouthe _____

1.030 forgyf _____

Complete these sentences (each answer, 3 points).

1.031 Chaucer lived in the _____ century.

1.032 The dialect that Modern English came from is the _____ dialect.

1.033 The Normans spoke _____ .

1.034 The leader and his men formed a _____ in Anglo-Saxon times.

1.035 The Anglo-Saxon monk who was a scholar and historian was _____ .

1.036 Gnomes are _____ .

1.037 The Anglo-Saxon word for *me* was _____ .

1.038 Middle English short _____ were nearly the same as those in Modern English.

1.039 The Crusades introduced Europe to a new _____ .

1.040 After 1066 many _____ words were added to the language.

Answer these questions (each answer, 5 points).

1.041 What was Sutton Hoo?

_____

_____

1.042 Why was Sutton Hoo important? _____

_____

_____

72 / 90   **SCORE** _____   **TEACHER** _____ _____

initials   date

ABC **Take your spelling test of Spelling Words-1.**

2. THE CONSTRUCTION OF SENTENCES

Sentences are the proper vehicles for expressing complete thoughts. Simple sentences, having one subject and one verb, are useful at times. Simple sentences may have compound subjects, compound predicates, or both. The constant use of simple sentences, however, may bore a reader or a listener. They may think that the writer or speaker is using a rather elementary level of expressing their thoughts. Often a person will want to combine related thoughts to avoid short, choppy sentences.

In this section, you will learn to combine sentences with other complete sentences or with part sentences. You will learn to identify and to form sentences by using coordinating conjunctions, correlative conjunctions, and conjunctive adverbs. You will learn to recognize and to construct sentences by using adverb clauses, adjective clauses, phrases, and appositives. You will also learn to spell correctly some new vocabulary words and to review the spelling of some familiar words.

SECTION OBJECTIVES

Review these objectives. When you have completed this section, you should be able to:

4. Identify and use correctly coordinate conjunctions, correlative conjunctions, and conjunctive adverbs.

5. Subordinate a lesser idea to a main idea by using an adverb clause, an adjective clause, a phrase, or an appositive.

8. Spell correctly some vocabulary words and some words with similar endings.

COORDINATION IN SENTENCES

Conveying exact meaning is a matter of carefully controlling sentences. Clarity and precision are necessary factors for sentence control. One method of creating a clear sentence is by the use of coordination. Coordination is the process of combining similar words, phrases, or clauses. Coordination is accomplished by the use of one of the three types of connectives: coordinate conjunctions, correlative conjunctions, and conjunctive adverbs. These connectives make sentences more precise by combining elements within the sentence or by combining two separate sentences.

Coordinate conjunctions. The most common connective is the coordinate conjunction. A list of the coordinate conjunctions follows.

By memorizing this list you will be able to identify and to use these connecting words correctly.

Coordinate conjunctions		
and	for	so
but	nor	yet
or		

Combining sentences or ideas by using a coordinate conjunction is simple. A coordinate conjunction must join only words, phrases, or clauses of *similar* usage. Nouns should be joined with nouns, verbs with verbs, and so on.

- **Right**: Roses *and* petunias bloomed profusely. (nouns)

- **Right**: Neither Jack *nor* Jill came. (nouns)

- **Wrong**: Roses *and* bloomed (noun and verb)

Joining the sentence with coordinate conjunctions helps the writer to express their thoughts *clearly* and *concisely.* In the following examples, two subjects are combined with a common verb to form one smooth sentence from two choppy ones.

Examples:

■ The woman looked sick. Her dog did, too.

■ Both the woman and her dog looked sick.

A writer may also combine closely related sentences into a single sentence with a subject or a verb in common.

Examples:

■ They felt worn out. They felt discouraged. They felt useless.

■ They felt worn out, discouraged, and useless.

Two separate sentences, or independent clauses, may be joined by a conjunction. The resulting *compound sentence* is a useful way to combine related ideas.

Examples:

■ I would rather eat cake here.

■ Joan wants to go out to eat.

■ I would rather eat cake here, *but* Joan wants to go out to eat.

Coordination by using coordinating conjunctions, then, is not difficult; it is one of the most common ways to combine words, phrases, and clauses.

Complete these activities.

2.1   List the coordinate conjunctions.

a. _____

b. _____

c. _____

d. _____

e. _____

f. _____

g. _____

2.2   Define these terms.

a. coordination _____

_____

b. compound sentence _____

_____

Coordinate any words, phrases, and clauses, in the following sentences by using coordinate conjunctions. You may write compound subjects, verbs, or other elements, or you may use compound sentences.

2.3   Joe likes sky diving. Mary does, too. _____

_____

2.4   I'll go to the Rockies. I'm afraid of heights. _____

_____

2.5   The last day of school is really hectic. That's the day most students like best!

_____

_____

2.6   "I'll have to take the bus. I won't fly." _____

2.7   The antique couch doesn't fit in Aunt Martha's trailer. The new dishwasher doesn't either.

_____

_____

2.8   That child can't go to school alone. I guess I'll have to take him.

_____

_____

2.9   You can go to the college your sister attended. You can choose a different college.

_____

_____

2.10   I enjoy eating fried chicken. I really like steak and french fries. My favorite food is lobster.

_____

_____

_____

2.11   The United States joined the coalition. The United Kingdom also joined. France would have nothing to do with it.

_____

_____

_____

Correlative conjunctions. Another method of coordination is accomplished by the use of correlative conjunctions. Correlatives are conjunctions used in pairs. These correlatives allow the writer to combine parallel ideas into sentences. The process of coordinating with correlative conjunctions is similar to that of coordinating with conjunctions. Words, phrases, and sentences may be combined as long as the elements being joined serve the same function.

Correlative Conjunctions

both	...	and
either	...	or
neither	...	nor
not only	...	but also
whether	...	or

In the following examples pairs of conjunctions work together by joining parallel words or phrases.

Example:

- The train is late. Maybe Martha missed it.

- *Either* the train is late, *or* Martha missed it.

The two clauses are effectively joined by the correlative conjunction *either ... or*. This use of conjunction pairs makes the sentence clear and the ideas parallel.

Example:

- Cucumbers make delicious pickles. Beets do, too.

- *Both* cucumbers *and* beets make delicious pickles.

In these examples the verb is retained and the subject becomes compound. The correlative pair, *both ... and*, allows the writer to combine the ideas, making one effective sentence from two weak ones.

Coordination with correlative conjunctions is quite simple. Although the correlatives are not used as frequently as coordinating conjunctions, they add variety to sentence structure.

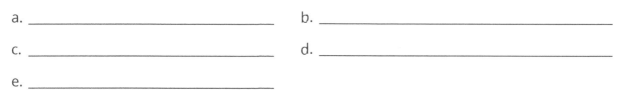

Complete this activity.

2.12   Give a list of the correlative conjunctions.

a. _____   b. _____

c. _____   d. _____

e. _____

Combine these sentences by using each of the correlative conjunctions at least once.

2.13   The manager of the supermarket will help the new employee. The assistant manager may help the employee, too.

_____

_____

2.14   The minister will not attend the meeting. The deacons won't attend either.

_____

_____

2.15   This award is given to junior high students. It is given to senior high students, too.

_____

_____

2.16   The Junior Varsity team is riding the bus to the play-off. The Varsity team is riding the same bus.

_____

_____

2.17   You may or may not go with us. It depends on your parents.

_____

_____

2.18   Help light the fire. Go help your brother collect wood.

_____

_____

2.19   Our kitten was affected by the new water. Our German Shepherd was also affected.

_____

_____

2.20   We may go sailing this Saturday. It depends on the weather.

_____

_____

2.21   Jerry enjoyed his trip through Italy. His sister, Karen, enjoyed it, too.

_____

_____

Conjunctive adverbs. The third type of connective is the conjunctive adverb, which is quite formal. It is used to coordinate two independent clauses rather than to combine two sentence parts into the same sentence. The conjunctive adverb functions not only as a conjunction but also as an adverb. As a conjunction it joins independent clauses, and as an adverb it modifies the independent clause in which it appears. The following is a list of conjunctive adverbs.

Conjunctive Adverbs

accordingly	furthermore	namely
also	hence	nevertheless
anyhow	however	otherwise
anyway	indeed	still
besides	instead	then
consequently	likewise	therefore
meanwhile	thus	moreover
so		

Unlike the conjunction, the conjunctive adverb may appear anywhere in the clause it modifies. Wherever the conjunctive appears, its major function is to join ideas. A conjunctive adverb can help a writer to express thoughts clearly and can provide variety in sentences.

In the following examples two clauses are joined to make a larger complete unit of thought. Notice that when a conjunctive adverb joins two main clauses, both a semicolon and a comma are used.

Example:

- The basic importance of Bible study is evident. Too many Christians today do not read it at all.

- The basic importance of Bible study is evident; *nevertheless*, too many Christians today do not read it at all.

Example:

- We don't have the money. We won't be going to the Olympics.

- We don't have the money; *therefore*, we won't be going to the Olympics.

Coordination is constantly used in both speaking and writing. Books and everyday speech contain examples of frequently used coordination.

The careful writer and speaker employs conjunctive adverbs sparingly. Overuse should be avoided. Coordination through the use of conjunctive adverbs is one helpful way to express ideas clearly.

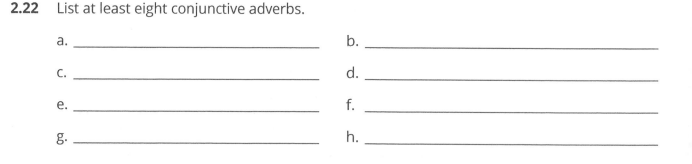

Complete this activity.

2.22 List at least eight conjunctive adverbs.

a. _____

b. _____

c. _____

d. _____

e. _____

f. _____

g. _____

h. _____

Coordinate these sentences by using ten different conjunctive adverbs.

2.23 The flowers on the altar were given to the church too late for the morning service. We'll use them in the evening service.

_____

_____

2.24 They wanted to go to New England this summer. They've saved for a whole year.

_____

2.25 He had a firm grip of the child's hand. She did not get lost in the crowd.

_____

2.26 We were going to try to find the rest of the party. No one seems to know which way they went. _____

_____

2.27 The nerve endings seem to be dead. The doctors will have to anesthetize the patient.

_____

2.28 The steaks in that restaurant are really tough. The vegetables are always cold.

_____

2.29 The kite was hopelessly tangled in the tree. The little girl's father struggled to get it down.

_____

_____

2.30 Early Christians were persecuted for their beliefs. We may be unpopular with certain friends for His sake.

_____

_____

2.31 The Christian life can be exciting. It can be quite fulfilling.

_____

_____

2.32 One commandment is to love the Lord completely. We have a lifetime task before us.

_____

_____

SUBORDINATION IN SENTENCES

The longer sentences become, the more ideas they can contain. The writer must arrange these ideas in logical order. The principal method for achieving clarity and smoothness in a sentence is through subordination, or using a less important idea to modify the main idea in the sentence.

- **Coordination**: It was a beautiful day, and we went swimming.
- **Subordination**: Since it was a beautiful day, we went swimming. (main idea: we went swimming)

Use adverb clauses, adjective clauses, phrases, and appositives to make one idea subordinate to another.

Adverb clauses. One of the more common methods of subordination is to use an adverb clause. An adverb clause can modify a verb, an adjective, or an adverb in the main clause. Adverb clauses help combine several thoughts or sentences into one sentence. An adverb clause begins with a subordinate conjunction. This subordinate conjunction is important for two reasons: it joins the adverb clause to the main clause, and it shows the relationship of the subordinate clause to the main clause. In fact, the process of choosing the exact subordinate conjunction for a precise meaning is the most important part of using adverb clauses.

You should become well acquainted with the following list of common subordinate conjunctions. Memorizing this list will make using adverb clauses much easier.

Subordinate Conjunctions

after	before	unless
although	if	until
as	in order that	when
as if	provided that	whenever
as long as	since	where
as soon as	so that	whereas
because	than	wherever
	though	while

Some of the words in this list can be used as other parts of speech. For example, the words *after, as, before, since,* and *until* can also be used as prepositions. These subordinate conjunctions express certain relationships between the adverb clause and the main clause.

Time relationship is expressed by the words *after, before, since, until, when, whenever,* and *while.*

Examples:

- *Since* he had his ear operation, Tim has even better hearing.
- *Whenever* I swim, I get severe leg cramps.

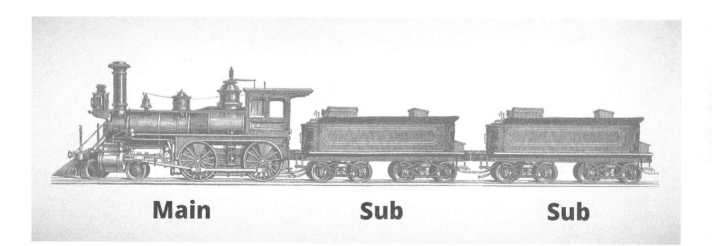

Main   **Sub**   **Sub**

Cause or reason relationship is expressed by the words *as, because, since,* and *whereas.*

Examples:

■ The newspaper reporters left *because* none of them could see the ambassador.

■ *Since* none of you has given an answer, I will be forced to look for it myself.

Purpose or result relationship is expressed by the words *that, in order that,* and *so that.*

Examples:

■ He spent more time studying *so that* he could be a better witness to his friends.

■ Jesus died *that* none would perish.

Condition relationship is expressed by the words *although, provided that, unless,* and *if.*

Examples:

■ *If* a person has the drive to excel in sports, he or she has the same opportunity of winning as anyone else.

■ I'll go with you to town, *although* I am tired.

Most adverb clauses are set off from the rest of the sentence by a comma.

Whatever subordinate conjunction you choose, you can be assured that both your ability to combine sentences and your writing ability will improve with practice.

 Complete this activity.

2.33   List ten subordinating conjunctions.

a. _____   b. _____

c. _____   d. _____

e. _____   f. _____

g. _____   h. _____

i. _____   j. _____

Combine these sentences with adverb clauses using the appropriate subordinate conjunction.

2.34   You obviously like cake. You never miss a sale at the bakery!

_____

2.35   Julie hates boating. Take her to the marina cafe, and we'll use the boat.

_____

_____

2.36   The church needs more money. It needs to continue to support missionaries.

_____

_____

2.37   Dad told me I could have all my privileges. I am almost ready to accept the responsibility of being a man.

_____

_____

2.38   We ignore the simple truths of the Bible. We will suffer greatly as a nation.

_____

_____

2.39   I don't get to sleep in my own room. My great aunt Sally visits us often and sleeps

in my room. _____

_____

2.40   The thunderstorm is over. We go out and gather the rain water that has accumulated

in the vats. _____

_____

2.41   I seem to work on homework more than ever. I don't really mind most of it.

_____

2.42   The highway ran right through the old park. It wouldn't have to circle five miles out of its way.

_____

2.43   They wanted us to go surfing with them. We were experts!

_____

Another effective method of subordination is by the use of the adjective clause, a subordinate clause used as an adjective to modify a noun or pronoun. The adjective clause, often called a relative clause, usually begins with a relative pronoun. This clause gives important information about the word it modifies. Since an adjective clause is subordinate, it is placed near the word it modifies. The purpose of the adjective clause is to provide additional information within that same sentence.

Study the following list of relative pronouns.

Relative Pronouns

| who | whose | that | whom | which |

Frequently the subject or object of the subordinate clause is the relative pronoun. Sometimes the relative pronoun may be omitted if it is not used as a subject.

Example:

■ A person _who_ listens carefully, learns much.

Adjective clauses. Adjective clauses can combine two choppy sentences into one clear, expressive sentence.

Examples:

- The flood came upon us without warning. It roared right through the canyon.
- The flood *that roared through the canyon* came upon us without warning.
- Fort Augustine was taken by the British. It once belonged to Spain.
- Fort Augustine, *which once belonged to Spain*, was taken over by the British.

Adjective clauses may be restrictive (necessary for identification of the word) or nonrestrictive (unnecessary). A restrictive clause is not set off by commas.

- **Restrictive**: The car that has a dented fender is mine. (which car)
- **Restrictive**: The boy who is in red is my brother. (which boy)
- **Nonrestrictive**: The yellow, 1970 Camaro, which has a dented fender, is mine. (The car has been identified without the adjective clause.)
- **Nonrestrictive**: My brother Matt, who is in red, is here. (He has already been identified.)

Who, whom, and *whose* all refer to people. They may be restrictive or nonrestrictive. *Which* and *that* refer to things. *Which* should be used in nonrestrictive clauses and *that* in restrictive clauses.

Using the five relative pronouns, create your own adjective clauses for these partial sentences.

2.44 The whistle of the five o'clock train, _____ , told us we were late.

2.45 Doctor Griffith, _____ , worked until dawn to save the baby's life.

2.46 Troy's parents, _____ , were proud to receive his trophy for him.

2.47 The high-speed racer _____ lost his last race.

2.48 The mountain _____ has always been a challenge to climbers around the world.

2.49 The stereo set, _____ , is carefully controlled by my father.

2.50 Mr. Morrison runs the newspaper _____ .

2.51 The high school play cast was given a standing ovation by a crowd

_____ .

2.52 We wore costumes, _____ , to the party.

2.53 The small boy _____ fell from Dusty's tree house.

Write _R_ for restrictive or _N_ for nonrestrictive.

2.54 _____ Greg Jones, who is my brother, is tall.

2.55 _____ The puppy that came to our back door was cold and hungry.

2.56 _____ The car that was stolen from the parking lot this morning was found.

2.57 _____ The last storm of the season, which was quite fierce, destroyed two bridges.

2.58 _____ The newspaper that is published by our school is quite popular.

LANGUAGE ARTS 806

LIFEPAC TEST

NAME _____

DATE _____

SCORE _____

68 / 85

LANGUAGE ARTS 806: LIFEPAC TEST

Write the letter of the correct answer. You may use an answer more than once (each answer, 2 points).

1. _____ yet
2. _____ either … or
3. _____ consequently
4. _____ still
5. _____ whether … or
6. _____ therefore
7. _____ after
8. _____ for
9. _____ as long as
10. _____ however

a. correlative conjunction
b. coordinate conjunction
c. conjunctive adverb
d. subordinate conjunction

Complete these sentences (each blank, 3 points).

11. The Norman Conquest of England occurred in the year _____ .

12. Early settlers of Britain were called _____ .

13. An Anglo-Saxon ship burial was found at _____ .

14. The most famous *epic* in the Old English language is _____ .

15. A poem, such as the "Seafarer" or the "Ruin," dealing with a serious subject is called

    _____ .

16. An Anglo-Saxon king who was a soldier and scholar was _____ .

17. Northumbrian is a _____ of the Anglo-Saxon language.

18. The Normans spoke the _____ language.

19. Two pronouns which have remained unchanged from Old English are

    a. _____ and b. _____ .

20. The Old English word *hwaer* means _____ .

Answer true or false (each answer, 1 point).

21. _____ Coordinates should join like words, phrases, or clauses.

22. _____ A subordinate clause is less important than a main clause.

23. _____ A nonrestrictive clause should not be set off by commas.

24. _____ An adverb clause usually begins with a relative pronoun.

25. _____ An appositive is a useful way to subordinate ideas.

26. _____ Jesse Stuart taught at Landsburgh High School.

27. _____ Several of Stuart's students had been in the first grade for as many as eight years.

28. _____ Admiral Byrd's air exploration of the North Pole region was successful.

29. _____ Byrd's trip, which began Thanksgiving Day, marked the first time any American had been within one thousand miles of the area.

30. _____ McKinley, Balchen, and Nansen accompanied Byrd.

Define these terms (each answer, 4 points).

31. autobiography _____

_____

_____

_____

32. turning point _____

_____

_____

_____

33. theme _____

_____

_____

_____

Answer these questions (each answer, 5 points).

34.   What contributions did Anglo-Saxon England make to language and culture?

_____

_____

_____

_____

_____

35.   What benefits can come from reading an autobiography?

_____

_____

_____

_____

_____

ABC **Take your LIFEPAC Spelling Test**

Phrases and appositives. A final method of subordination is by using phrases and appositives. These sentence elements may be used to combine ideas into more concise sentences. Phrases and appositives have one significant advantage over subordinate clauses—they are shorter.

All types of phrases may be used to combine two sentences into one. The writer may achieve clarity and still remain concise.

- **Example**: The dentist left. He has a new car.
- **Prepositional phrases**: The dentist left in his new car.
- **Example**: Sally ran into class. She forgot her pen.
- **Participial phrase**: Forgetting her pen, Sally ran into class.

More than one type of phrase may be used to combine two or more sentences into one. Be careful to place each phrase close to the word or words it modifies.

- **Example**: It was late evening. The waitresses locked the doors. They were getting ready to go.
- **Prepositional phrase**: In the evening the waitresses locked the doors
- **Participial phrase**: getting ready to go home.

Subordination by using appositives is also a helpful combining technique. An appositive is a word or phrase which follows a noun and helps to explain it; the appositive means the same thing as a noun it follows—they are interchangeable. The appositive, like the phrase, permits the writer to subordinate an idea, allowing them to unclutter their writing by eliminating unnecessary sentences.

- **Example**: Joan Phillips will take the first chair at the district concert. She is a violinist in our orchestra.
- **Appositive**: Joan Phillips, a violinist in our orchestra, will take the first chair at the district concert.
- **Example**: Coach Moore gave the squad a week off. Only the varsity had the week off.
- **Appositive**: Coach Moore gave the squad, varsity only, a week off.

Coordinating or subordinating related ideas into sentences will prevent your speech or writing from sounding short, choppy, or immature. Remember that improper or overused coordination or subordination is worse than none at all. All of these methods, properly used, can provide sentence variety and effectiveness.

Combine the statements into one clear sentence by using phrases or appositives.

2.59 We were near the cave. We came across bear cubs. They were growling for food.

_____

_____

2.60 The car is an antique. It will use fifteen gallons of gasoline for a two hundred-mile trip. It uses ten sometimes. _____

_____

2.61   The church picnic was held on Independence Day. It was a feast. It attracted many teens. The teens were mostly our age. _____

_____

2.62   I was in a restaurant on the turnpike. I met a person from my hometown. He had been my grandfather's doctor. _____

_____

Identify the italicized words by writing *A* for appositive or *P* for phrase.

2.63   _____   Our graduation party, *a memorable event held in the Fellowship Hall*, was enjoyable for the entire class.

2.64   _____   We enjoy making maple syrup *in the spring*.

2.65   _____   Mrs. Miller, our gym teacher, encourages us by *letting us use the equipment after school.*

2.66   _____   By keeping our dog inside, we help our postman, *Mr. Mack*.

2.67   _____   Sandy, *my best friend,* goes shell hunting with me on the East coast.

SPELLING

Some English words are not spelled the way they sound. Many words are not pronounced the way they are spelled. Knowing how to correctly pronounce even the more difficult English words is necessary for proper communication.

The following list contains some of the most commonly mispronounced words in the English language. Learn how to spell and correctly pronounce each word in this list.

Spelling Words-2		
amiable	irrelevant	prerogative
athletic	irreverent	probably
barbarous	lightning	tentative
brethren	laboratory	tragedy
burglary	mathematician	sacrilegious
disastrous	mischievous	suffrage
formally	momentous	surprise
formerly	perform	undoubtedly
government		

Write the letter of the spelling word that matches each numbered definition.

2.68	_____ irreverent	a.	amiable
2.69	_____ harmful, troublesome	b.	barbarous
2.70	_____ uncivilized	c.	formerly
2.71	_____ friendly	d.	irrelevant
2.72	_____ important, of consequence	e.	mischievous
2.73	_____ special right, privilege	f.	prerogative
2.74	_____ right to vote, franchise	g.	tentative
2.75	_____ in time past	h.	sacrilegious
2.76	_____ inapplicable	i.	suffrage
2.77	_____ provisional, temporary	j.	momentous

Look up the dictionary pronunciation of these words. Repeat them correctly to yourself as you write them.

2.78 burglary _____

2.79 brethren _____

2.80 formally _____

2.81 government _____

2.82 irreverent _____

2.83 lightning _____

2.84 laboratory _____

2.85 perform _____

2.86 probably _____

2.87 tragedy _____

Unscramble the following spelling words.

2.88 ventaetti _____

2.89 blameia _____

2.90 afrusefg _____

2.91 entuommos _____

2.92 graylurb _____

2.93 mongrevnet _____

Write ten original sentences using the following words.

2.94 mathematician _____

2.95 undoubtedly _____

2.96 surprise _____

2.97 disastrous _____

2.98 athletic _____

2.99 lightning _____

2.100 mischievous _____

2.101 formerly _____

2.102 formally _____

2.103 irreverent _____

2.104 irrelevant _____

2.105 tentative _____

ABC **Ask your teacher to give you a practice spelling test of Spelling Words-2.** Restudy the words you missed.

↺ **Review the material in this section in preparation for the Self Test.** This Self Test will check your mastery of this particular section as well as your knowledge of the previous section.

SELF TEST 2

Write the letter of the answer to each numbered term (each answer, 2 points).

2.01 _____ London   a. Danish king

2.02 _____ Celts   b. 1066

2.03 _____ *Beowulf*   c. earliest inhabitants of Briton

2.04 _____ "The Wanderer"   d. ship-burial

2.05 _____ Chaucer   e. *Canterbury Tales*

2.06 _____ Hrothgar   f. 449

2.07 _____ Alfred   g. a dialect that became the standard

2.08 _____ Norman Conquest   h. an elegy

2.09 _____ French   i. a riddle

2.010 _____ Sutton Hoo   j. Anglo-Saxon king

     k. Anglo-Saxon epic

     l. influenced Middle English vocabulary

Complete the following sentences (each blank, 3 points).

2.011 Three types of connectives include a. _____ , b. _____ ,

and c. _____ .

2.012 A subordinate clause is _____ important than the main clause.

2.013 Four ways to subordinate an idea include a. _____ ,

b. _____ , c. _____ , and d. _____ .

2.014 A major rule in coordinating sentences is that a writer must coordinate elements that

_____ .

2.015 Pairs of conjunctions used to create parallel ideas are called _____

_____ .

Write on each blank the letter for the correct answer (each answer, 2 points).

2.016 Subordination is a way of placing less important ideas or facts into _____ .
a. clauses   b. phrases   c. appositives   d. a, b, and c

2.017 One of the most common methods of subordination is the use of _____ .
a. the adjective clause   b. the adverb clause
c. the relative clause   d. the appositive phrase

2.018 The conjunction that shows a time relationship is _____ .
a. than   b. because   c. since   d. although

2.019 The conjunction that shows a cause or reason relationship is _____ .
a. so that   b. wherever   c. after   d. because

2.020 The conjunction that shows a result relationship is _____ .
a. so that   b. where   c. since   d. before

2.021 The conjunction that shows a condition relationship is _____ .
a. if   b. until   c. as   d. while

2.022 A clause that begins with a relative pronoun is a/an _____ clause.
a. adjective   b. independent   c. adverbial   d. appositive

Complete the following lists (each answer, 1 point).

2.023 Four coordinate conjunctions

a. _____ b. _____

c. _____ d. _____

2.024 Four correlative conjunctions

a. _____ b. _____

c. _____ d. _____

2.025 Six conjunctive adverbs

a. _____ b. _____

c. _____ d. _____

e. _____ f. _____

Answer these questions (each answer, 5 points).

2.026 What is an elegy? _____

_____

2.027 What was the *comitatus*? _____

_____

_____

70 / 88   SCORE _____   TEACHER _____ _____

initials   date

ABC **Take your spelling test of Spelling Words-2.**

3. THE AUTOBIOGRAPHY

One of the most interesting and often exciting types of literature is autobiography. Through reading autobiographical accounts, the reader can experience events, participate in the making of history, or explore vast wildernesses without ever leaving his chair.

In this section, you will learn to look for several elements that are used in autobiography. You will read two very different accounts of real people. One autobiography is about an old-fashioned one-room school. The other account describes part of Admiral Byrd's exploration of the icy wasteland of Antarctica. You will also learn the meaning and spelling of several new vocabulary words.

SECTION OBJECTIVES

Review these objectives. When you have completed this section, you should be able to:

6. Identify basic elements usually included in an autobiography.

7. Describe the characteristics of autobiography.

8. Spell correctly some vocabulary words and some words with similar endings.

VOCABULARY

Study these words to enhance your learning success in this section.

narrative (nar'u tiv). A story or an account of someone or something.

theme (thēm). The topic or main idea of a story.

THE ELEMENTS OF THE AUTOBIOGRAPHY

An autobiography is a story a person writes about his own life. It is connected **narrative**, revealing the author's personal feelings.

An autobiography contains certain elements which the reader should notice. One of these elements is the setting or location of the autobiography. Often the location will have a great influence on the author. A writer who lives in New England will tend to use in their writing the traditions and language patterns typical of their geographic location. A person writing about a shipwreck or about life in the jungle would certainly deal with setting. In some books, however, the location of the autobiography is irrelevant.

Another closely related element is the significance of time—the historical events affecting the writer. If political or social conditions are mentioned in the autobiography, the reader should be aware of their impact. For example, *The Diary of Anne Frank* is greatly affected by political events at the time—Hitler's persecution of the Jews and World War II.

A third element to notice is the author's personal life—home life, family, and friends, may be mentioned through anecdotes. Since an autobiography is highly personal, it offers the reader many valuable insights into the author's attitudes, feelings, and experiences. People and incidents usually have tremendous effect on the author of an autobiography. These personal glimpses are the reader's opportunity to discover the personality of the author and to understand the events that have motivated them.

An element closely related to the previous one is the description of the author's awareness of significant moments—*turning points*—in life. These major turning points may have resulted in success or failure. They may have caused the author to develop courage or perseverance. The reader has the opportunity to assess, or judge, the effect of these significant moments upon the author's life.

The final element, the most significant to the reader, is the **theme**. The author has recorded personal events and feelings to share with the readers. They have stated a truth about life as they see it. The success or failure of the autobiography depends not upon the amount of book sales but upon the effect of the book upon the reader. A well-written autobiography may inspire the reader to have faith, courage, dependability, or other valuable qualities of character. The most important element of autobiography is the book's significance to the reader's personal life—the influence it exerts upon the reader's reactions to situations in the future after reading the book. The reader must critically evaluate the author's theme to see if they agree or disagree with the author's view of life.

"The Thread That Runs So True." The following excerpt is from an autobiography by Jesse Stuart. Notice the personal glimpses given by this young school teacher who learns that sometimes a person must defend his convictions. Through his students and through his experiences, this young man learns valuable lessons about success and failure in life. Notice this man's struggles and the way he overcomes obstacles as he builds his own character while he works to increase the knowledge and to build the characters of his unruly students.

In any new story new vocabulary words are certain to confuse the reader unless he becomes familiar with those as he reads. The following list is vocabulary words from the "The Thread That Runs So True." Be able to correctly spell and pronounce each word.

tenor (as used in story)	prominent
elongated	galvanized
controversies	census
cistern	subsistence
vaguely	recitation
reluctantly	

THE THREAD THAT RUNS SO TRUE

Monday morning when I started on my way to school, I had with me Don Conway, a pupil twenty years of age, who had never planned to enter school again. I was the new teacher here at Lonesome Valley, and I didn't know what kind of brains he had. He had left school when he was in the fourth grade. But I did know that he had two good fists and that he would be on my side. All day Sunday while I had worked at the schoolhouse, I was trying to think of a plan so I could stay at Lonesome Valley School. I knew I had to stay. I knew if one had to go it would be Guy Hawkins. I might have to use my head a little but that was why I had it.

It had taken a lot of persuasion to get Don Conway to return to school. He had planned to get married after his tobacco crop was sold. But I explained the value of an education to him in dollars and cents. I told him I would teach him how to measure a field and figure the number of acres, how to figure the number of bushels in a wagon bed or cornbin, and how many cubic yards of dirt one would have to remove to dig a cellar or a well. Don Conway was interested in this type of knowledge. I told him no man should be married and live on a farm unless he knew these simple things, for he could easily be cheated the rest of his days. I was interested in his learning these things all right, but I was interested in something else.

Don, his two small brothers, his sister Vaida, and I went to school together. I congratulated John Conway for sending all his children but one. I told him he should set the example for other farmers on the creek. It would have been hard on John to try to worm and sucker his ten acres of tobacco and care for his other crops if Flossie, his older daughter, had not volunteered to help him. And Bertha, his wife, assured him she would divide her time between the housework and work in the field.

Flossie, eighteen years old, who had left school six years ago, would gladly have started back to school if I had insisted. But I knew John and Bertha had to have someone left to help them. I insisted and almost begged Don to return to school when he and I were sitting on the porch late one Sunday afternoon and Ova Salyers and Guy Hawkins rode past on their horses. They glanced toward the porch for their first look at the new teacher, never spoke but rode silently down the road.

Don Conway looked at Guy Hawkins and Ova Salyers and then he looked at me. He didn't ask me how old I was. I didn't tell him in eighteen more days I would be seventeen. One had

to be eighteen before he was old enough to teach school. Don Conway knew the fate of my sister when she was employed to teach the Lonesome Valley School. He knew how Guy Hawkins had blacked her eyes with his fists, had whipped her before the Lonesome Valley pupils. She was a fair-haired, beautiful, blue-eyed girl of nineteen when she had come to Lonesome Valley. She went home a nervous wreck, long before her school was finished. After I'd seen the way my sister was beaten up, I begged to go to Lonesome Valley. My parents would have none of it. They thought if I went hunting trouble I would get more than my share…. Then I had John Hampton, a rural teacher and friend, contact John Conway and get the school for me. Superintendent Staggers didn't want me to go to Lonesome Valley. But there wasn't anything he could do about it after John Conway, Lonesome Valley District School trustee, recommended me. That was why I was here to teach school.

When Don and I reached the schoolhouse, at least thirty-five pupils were there waiting outside. Guy Hawkins and Ova Salyers were standing together near the coal house with their torn and tattered first-grade books. They looked out of place with the other pupils. They were larger than either Don or me. They were older too. They looked at me when I said "Good morning" to them. Many of the pupils turned shyly away and did not speak. They were waiting for the schoolhouse to be unlocked so they could rush in and select their seats. Each had his dinner basket or bucket in his hand. The majority of them carried tattered-edged and backless books.

The girls wore pigtails down their backs tied with all colors of ribbons. They wore clean print dresses and they were barefooted. Not one pupil in my school, large or small, boy or girl, wore a pair of shoes. I'd never seen in my life so many barefooted people, young, middle-aged, and old, as I had seen in Lonesome Valley. Wearing gloves on their hands in summer was the same to them as wearing shoes on their feet. They just didn't do it.

"Well, I'm opening the door," I said, to break the silence of my pupils.

When I opened the door, they laughed, screamed, and raced for the schoolhouse. Their shyness was gone now. There was a mad scramble to get inside the schoolhouse for seats. Then there was some discussion among them as to who would sit by whom. Girls had selected their seatmates. There were a few controversies and a few hurt feelings. Often two pupils wanted to sit by the same person. No trouble with Guy and Ova. They walked inside reluctantly and sat down in a seat on the boys' side farthest from my desk.

"Now let me make an announcement to you before school starts," I said, after walking up to my desk. "There will not any longer be a girls' side and a boys' side. Sit any place you want to."

They looked strangely at one another. Not one boy would cross to the girls' side. Not one girl would cross to the boys' side. In Lonesome Valley it was hard to break a teaching tradition more than a century old. But after I had been to high school, where there were no such things as a girls' side and a boys' side in a schoolroom, I didn't see why it wouldn't work in Lonesome Valley. Little did I dream that what I had said here would make news in Lonesome Valley, that it would be talked

about by everybody, and that many would criticize me and call my school "a courting school." Boys and girls sitting together? Who had ever heard tell of it?

When I walked down the broad center aisle and pulled on the bell rope, the soft tones sounded over the tobacco, corn, and cane fields and the lush green valley; with the ringing of this bell, my school had begun. I knew that not half the pupils in the school census were here. There were one hundred and four in the school census, of school age, for whom the state sent per capita money to pay for their schooling. I had thirty-five pupils. I thought the soft tones of this school bell through the rising mists and over warm cultivated fields where parents and their children were trying to eke out a bare subsistence from the soil might bring back warm memories of happy school days. For I remembered the tones of the Plum Grove school bell, and how I had longed to be back in school after I had quit at the age of nine to work for twenty-five cents a day to help support my family. If I could have, I would have returned to school when I heard the Plum Grove bell. So I rang the bell and called the Lonesome Valley pupils back to school—back to books and play. For going to school had never been work to me. It had been recreation. And I hoped it would be the same for my pupils in Lonesome Valley.

When I dismissed my pupils for the first recess, a fifteen-minute period between the beginning of the school day and the noon hour, I was amazed to see them all jump up from their seats at the same time and try to be first out of the house. Big pupils pushed past the little ones, and there was so much confusion and disorder I knew they would never leave the room like this again. Why were they running? I wondered. I had a few minutes' work to do before I could join them on the playground. Before I had finished this work, I heard the tenor of their uneven voices singing these familiar words:

The needle's eye that does supply,
The thread that runs so true,
Many a beau have I let go,
Because I wanted you.

Many a dark and stormy night,
When I went home with you,
I stumped my toe and down I go,
Because I wanted you.

I walked to the door and watched them. They had formed a circle, hand in hand, and around and around they walked and sang these words while two pupils held their locked hands high for the circle to pass under. Suddenly the two standing—one inside the circle and one outside—let their arms drop down to take a pupil from the line. Then the circle continued to march and sing while the two took the pupil aside and asked him whether he would rather be a train or an automobile. If the pupil said he'd rather be an automobile, he stood on one side; if a train, he stood on the other

of the two that held hands. And when they had finished taking everybody from the circle, the two groups faced each other, lined up behind their captains. Each put his arms around the pupil in front of him and locked his hands. The first line to break apart or to be pulled forward lost the game.

Fifteen minutes were all too short for them to play "the needle's eye." I let recess extend five minutes so they could finish their second game. It had been a long time since I had played this game at Plum Grove. These words brought back pleasant memories. They fascinated me. And my Lonesome Valley pupils played this game with all the enthusiasm and spirit they had! They put themselves into it—every pupil in school. Not one stood by to watch. Because they were having the time of their lives, I hated to ring the bell for "books." I lined them up, smaller pupils in front and larger ones behind, and had them march back into the schoolroom.

Guy Hawkins and Ova Salyers were the last on the line. When they came inside the door, Guy asked permission to go with Ova after a bucket of water. We didn't

have a well or a cistern at the schoolhouse. We had to get water from some home in the district. I told them they could go but not to be gone too long, for the pupils, after running and playing, were thirsty. The July sun beat down on the galvanized tin roof. This made the pine boards so hot inside they oozed resin. We raised all the windows, but still the place was hot as the room in which I slept at Conways'. My little room upstairs with a high unscreened window of only one sash didn't cool off until about midnight. Then I could go to sleep.

The first bucket of water Guy and Ova brought didn't last five minutes. The majority of the pupils were still thirsty. I sent Guy and Ova back for more, telling them to borrow another bucket. I sent them in a hurry. And I knew I had to do something about the dipper problem. At Plum Grove, too, we had all drunk from the same dipper, but when I went to Landsburgh High School I was taught something different.

So I made "an important announcement" to my pupils. I told them each had to bring his own drinking cup the next day.

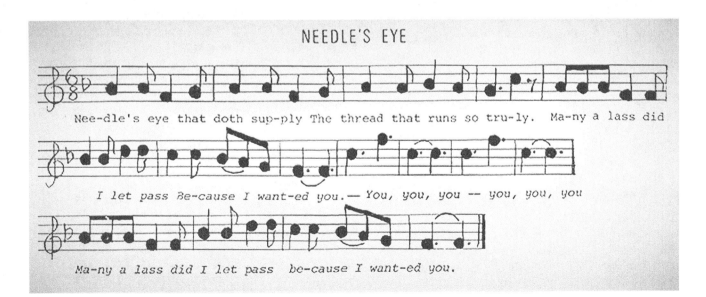

It could be a glass, teacup, gourd, dipper, just so it was his own and no one else drank from it. My pupils looked at one another and laughed as if my announcement was funny. But I had seen sweat run from their faces into the dipper, and the next in line put his mouth where the sweat had run or where the other pupil had put his lips. I noticed, too, several pupils had put the rim up near the handle to their mouths, so I knew they didn't like to drink after the others.

On Tuesday they brought their dippers, tin cups, and glasses. Only a few had forgotten, and I stopped with my busy schedule of classwork long enough to teach them how to make paper drinking cups. I showed them how to take a clean sheet of paper from a tablet and fold it to hold water. I gave them a lecture about drinking water. I told them never to drink from a stream. I told them how I had gotten typhoid fever twice: once from drinking cool water from a little stream, and once from drinking in a river. I had my pupils use the dipper to dip water from the bucket into their cups. They accepted my suggestion gladly. I also borrowed another water bucket from Bertha Conway and brought it to school. The one bucket allowed me for thirty-five pupils (and there would be more as soon as the farmers were through with their summer plowing and worming and suckering tobacco, stripping their cane and boiling the juice to syrup) was not enough. They played hard at recess and noon and in the "time of books" sat in a schoolroom almost as hot as an oven.

Tuesday when I stood beside Guy Hawkins and showed him how to hold his book when he read, my pupils laughed until I had to stop them. I was trying to teach Guy to read as he stumbled over the simple words in the First Grade Reader. My pupils laughed because Guy was taller by two inches than I was and heavier. He had a bullneck almost as large as his head, and a prominent jaw. His beard was so heavy that he had to shave every day.

Wouldn't Coach Wilson like to have him! I thought. He would make the best tackle Landsburgh High School ever had.

Guy had big hands. His right hand covered the back of his First Reader. And he had powerful arms. The muscles rippled under his clean blue-faded shirt. I measured him as I stood beside him. I knew that if I ever had to fight him, it would be a fight. And I knew that I wasn't going to fight him unless he forced me to fight. He was more powerful physically than I was. And the outcome of our fight might depend on the one who successfully landed the first haymaker to the other's jaw.

Then I looked down at Ova Salyers sitting on the recitation seat beside me. Another tackle for Coach Wilson, I thought. This pair would be a coach's dream. Pity some coach doesn't have 'em instead of me.

If it were not for these two young men, I wouldn't have had any trouble disciplining my school. All the other pupils played hard and they were obedient. They would have been good in their class work if they had had the proper training. I had ten-year old pupils just starting to school. Nineteen-year-olds in the first grade. Fourteen-year-olds in the second grade. I had one twelve-year-old girl in the eighth grade. They had not been promoted because they had never attended a full school term. They had taken the same grade over and over until they could stand

and recite some of the beginning lessons from memory.

"Guy, how long have you been in the first grade?" I asked.

"Oh, about eight years," he laughed.

"You're not going to be in it any longer," I said.

"Why?" he asked.

"Because I'm going to promote you," I said. "Tomorrow you start in the second grade."

Then I had Ova Salyers read. He had also been in the first grade eight years. I promoted him.

When these young men sat down again I saw them look at each other and laugh as if they thought my promoting them was funny. I knew they accepted school as a joke, a place to come and see people. A place where they could join a circle of smaller children and play "the needle's eye." And I knew there wasn't much chance of reasoning with either one. But I had a feeling that time would come. I didn't believe they were coming to school for any good. I felt that Guy was waiting his chance for me. I was not going to take any chances; I was going to give him the full benefit of the doubt.

The following Monday I had stayed at the schoolhouse to do some work on my school records, and Don Conway had gone home with his sister and brothers. This was the first afternoon I had stayed at school after all my pupils had gone. The room was very silent, and I was busy working when I heard soft footsteps walking around the building. I looked through the window on my left and I saw Guy Hawkins' head. His uncombed, tousled hair was ruffled by the Lonesome Valley wind.

I wondered why he was coming back. I wondered if he had forgotten something.

Then I realized this was the first time he had been able to catch me by myself. And I remembered a few other incidents in Greenwood County's rural schools where a pupil had come back to the school when the teacher was there alone, and had beaten the tar out of him. I could recall three or four such incidents. But I didn't have time to think about them. Not now. Guy came in the door with his cap in his hand. I didn't want him to see me looking up at him, but I did see him coming down the broad middle aisle, taking long steps and swinging his big arms. He looked madder than any man or animal I had ever seen. He walked up to my desk and stood silently before me.

"Did you forget something, Guy?" I asked.

"Naw, I've never forgot nothin'," he reminded me.

"Then what do you want?" I asked.

"Whip you," he said.

"Why do you want to whip me?" I asked him.

"I didn't like your sister," he said. "You know what I done to her."

"Yes, I know what you did to her," I said.

"I'm a-goin' to do the same thing to you," he threatened.

"Why do you want to fight me?" I asked him. I dropped my pencil and stood up facing him.

"I don't like you," he said. "I don't like teachers. I said never another person with your name would teach this school. Not as long as I'm here."

"It's too bad you don't like me or my name," I said, my temper rising.

"I won't be satisfied until I've whipped you," he said.

"Can you go to another school?" I asked him. "Sandy Valley School is not too far from where you live."

"Naw, naw," he shouted, "if anybody leaves, you'll leave. I was in Lonesome Valley first. And I ain't a-goin to no other school because of you!"

"Then there's nothing left for us to do but fight," I said. "I've come to teach this school, and I'm going to teach it!"

"Maybe you will," he snarled. "I have you penned in this schoolhouse. I have you where I want you. You can't get away! You can't run! I aim to whip you right where you stand! It's the same place where I whipped your sister!"

I looked at his face. It was red as a sliced beet. Fire danced in his pale blue, elongated eyes. I knew Guy Hawkins meant every word he said. I knew I had to face him and to fight. There was no other way around. I had to think quickly. How would I fight him?

"Will you let me take my necktie off?" I said, remembering I'd been choked by a fellow pulling my necktie once in a fight.

"Yep, take off that purty tie," he said. "You might get it dirty by the time I'm through with you."

I slowly took off my tie.

"Roll up the sleeves of your white shirt too," he said. "But they'll be dirty by the time I sweep this floor up with you."

"Sweep the floor up with me," I said.

He shot out his long arm but I ducked. I felt the wind from his thrust against my ear.

I mustn't let him clinch me, I thought.

Then he came back with another right and I ducked his second lick. I came around with my first lick—a right—and planted it on his jaw, not a good lick but just enough to jar him and make him madder. When he rushed at me, I sidestepped. He missed. By the time he had turned around, I caught him a haymaker on the chin that reeled him. Then I followed up with another lick as hard as I had ever hit a man. Yet I didn't bring him down. He came back for more. But he didn't reach me this time. He was right. I did get my shirt dirty. I dove through the air with a flying tackle. I hit him beneath the knees. I'd tackled like this in football. I'd tackled hard. And I never tackled anybody harder than Guy. His feet went from under him, and I scooted past on the pine floor. I'd tackled him so quickly when he had expected me to come back at him with my fists, that he went down so fast he couldn't catch with his hands. His face hit flat against the floor and his nose was flattened. The blood spurted as he started to get up.

I let him get to his feet. I wondered if I should. For I knew it was either him or me. One of us had to whip. When he did get to his feet after that terrible fall, I waded into him. I hit fast and I hit hard. He swung wild. His fingernail took a streak of hide from my neck and left a red mark that smarted, and the blood oozed through. I pounded his chin. I caught him on the beardy jaw. I reeled him back and followed up. I gave him a left to the short ribs while my right in a split second caught his mouth. Blood spurted again. Yet he was not through. But I knew I had him.

"Had enough?" I panted.

He didn't answer. I didn't ask him a second time. I hit him hard enough to knock two men down. I reeled him back against a seat. I followed up. I caught him with a haymaker under the chin and laid him across the desk. Then he rolled to the floor. He lay there with blood running from his nose and mouth. His eyes were rolled back. I was nearly out of breath. My hands ached. My heart pounded. If this is teaching school! I thought. If this goes with it! Then I remembered vaguely I had asked for it. I'd asked for this school. I would take no other.

Guy Hawkins lay there sprawled on the unswept floor. His blood was mingled with the yellow dirt carried into the schoolroom by seventy bare feet. I went back and got the water bucket. With a clean handkerchief, I washed blood from his mouth and nose. I couldn't wash it from his shirt. I put cool water to his forehead.

I worked over a pupil—trying to bring him back to his senses—whom only a few hours before I had stood beside and tried to teach how to pronounce words when he read. "Don't stumble over them like a horse stumbles over frozen ground," I told him, putting it in a language he would understand. I had promoted him. I'd sent Guy and Ova after water when other pupils had wanted to go. On their way to get water, I knew they … thought they were putting something over on me....

I had known the time would eventually come. But I wanted to put it off as long as I could. Now I had whipped him, and I wondered as I looked at him stretched on the floor how I'd done it. He was really knocked out for the count. I knew the place where we had fought would always be marked. It was difficult to remove bloodstain from pine wood. It would always be there, this reminder, as long as I taught school at Lonesome Valley.

When Guy Hawkins came to his senses, he looked up at me. I was applying the wet cool handkerchief to his head. When he started to get up, I helped him to his feet.

"Mr. Stuart, I really got it poured on me," he admitted. "You're some fighter."

This was the first time he had ever called me "Mr. Stuart." I had heard, but had pretended not to hear, him call me "Old Jess" every time my back was turned. He had never before, when he had spoken directly to me, called me anything.

"I'm not much of a fighter until I have to fight, Guy," I said. "You asked for it. There was no way round. I had to fight you."

"I know it," he said. "I've had in mind to whip you ever since I heard you's a-goin' to teach this school. But you win. You winned fair, too," he honestly admitted. "I didn't think you could hit like that."

Guy was still weak. His nose and mouth kept bleeding. He didn't have a handkerchief, and I gave him a clean one.

"Think you can make it home all right, Guy?"

"I think so," he said.

He walked slower from the schoolhouse than he had walked in. I was too upset to do any more work on my record book. I stood by the window and watched him walk across the schoolyard, then across the foot log and down the Lonesome Creek Road until he went around the bend and was out of sight. Something told me to watch for Ova Salyers. He might return to attack me. I waited several minutes, and Ova didn't come. Guy had come to do the job alone.

I felt better now that the fight was over, and I got the broom and swept the floor. I had quickly learned that the rural teacher was janitor as well, and that his janitor work was one of the important things in his school. I believed, after my brief experience, that the schoolhouse should be made a place of beauty, prettier and cleaner than any of the homes the pupils came from so they would love the house and the surroundings, and would think of it as a place of beauty and would want to keep it that way.

The floor was easy to sweep. But it was difficult to clean blood from the floor. I carried a coal bucket of sand and poured it on the blood and then shoveled up the sand and carried it out. I had the blood from the floor. Then I scrubbed the place, but the stain was there. I could not get it from the oily, soft pine wood. I knew this was one day in my teaching career I would never forget.

I didn't expect Guy Hawkins to return to Lonesome Valley School. I thought his schooling was ended. But when he left the schoolhouse he didn't take his books. I wondered if he would come back to get them, and, if he came, would he bring his father or one of his married brothers with him? Would he start another fight? The same thoughts must have troubled John

Conway. When I went to school on Tuesday morning, John went with me.

This was John Conway's first visit to the school, for his farm work had piled up on him since all of his children but Flossie were going to school. When we got there, big Guy Hawkins with his black eyes and swollen lips was in a circle with the other pupils, going around, and singing "The Needle's Eye." Guy greeted me: "Good morning, Mr. Stuart."

Then John Conway smiled and turned to go. I watched him cross the foot log and go into the little

store. I joined the game, "the needle's eye," with my pupils. Guy Hawkins and I were captains. I was the hard-boiled egg, the majority chose the soft-boiled egg. Guy Hawkins got three-fourths of the pupils. And when we formed our tug of war to pull against each other, his side toppled my side. They pulled us all over the yard, and everybody laughed, especially Guy Hawkins. It was great fun. And never did Guy Hawkins or a pupil ask me about the fight. If they talked about it, I didn't know. I did notice them observing the bloodstain on the floor. If Guy Hawkins ever

said anything against me to a fellow pupil again, I never heard of it. He had, for the first time, become a pupil like the rest. He had, for the first time, acted as if he was a part of our school.[1]

Complete these activities.

3.1 Briefly define *autobiography*. _____

_____

3.2 Explain the importance of each of the following elements of autobiography.

a. Location or setting:

_____

b. Time written (historical and political events):

_____

c. Personal life (friends, family, anecdotes):

_____

_____

d. Turning point(s): _____

_____

e. Theme: _____

_____

_____

---

[1]Jesse Stuart, "The Thread That Runs So True." From The Thread That Runs So True. Copyright © 1949 by Jesse Stuart.
*Used by permission of publishers, Charles Scribner's Sons.

✎ **Answer these questions.**

3.3 What is the setting or location of this story? What is the date?

a. _____   b. _____

3.4 How does the setting affect what can and does happen in this story?
(Think of some of the incidents and characters.)

_____

_____

_____

3.5 Is anything political happening in the United States that directly affects this story?

a. _____ (if so, what?) b. _____

3.6 What are four things Stuart reveals about his personality through some incidents, thoughts, or speech?

a. _____

b. _____

c. _____

d. _____

3.7 What is the turning point of this story?

_____

_____

_____

3.8 How does this incident affect the rest of the story?

_____

_____

_____

3.9 What do you think Stuart is trying to say to the reader?

_____

_____

_____

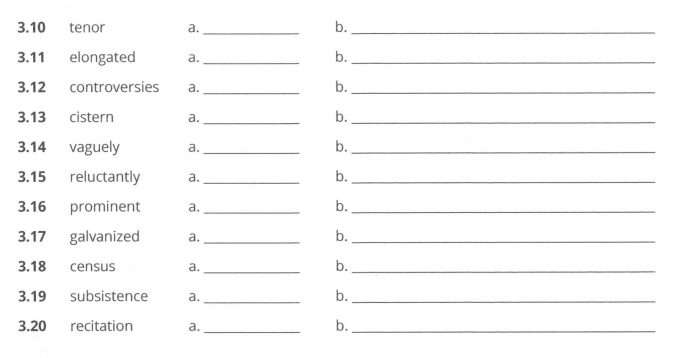

Look up each word in the dictionary. Write down its part of speech, then use each word in a sentence.

3.10 tenor a. _____ b. _____

3.11 elongated a. _____ b. _____

3.12 controversies a. _____ b. _____

3.13 cistern a. _____ b. _____

3.14 vaguely a. _____ b. _____

3.15 reluctantly a. _____ b. _____

3.16 prominent a. _____ b. _____

3.17 galvanized a. _____ b. _____

3.18 census a. _____ b. _____

3.19 subsistence a. _____ b. _____

3.20 recitation a. _____ b. _____

"Flight to the South Pole." The following auto-biography was written by Rear Admiral Richard E. Byrd, who made the first flight to the South Pole. As you read, underline or note examples of the *setting, incidents, character*, and *significant moments* or *turning points*. These elements all combine to form a good autobiography. Labeling these elements will help you to understand Admiral Byrd and what he experienced personally during this famous flight. Making notes or underlining will also help you answer the questions following this longer autobiography.

This autobiography contains quite a few new vocabulary words that are necessary to the understanding of the story. Knowing the part of speech and the meaning of these words also helps the reader to expand his own vocabulary. The following list contains vocabulary words from the story. Be able to correctly pronounce and spell each one.

scrupulous	profusion	perilously
consternation	chronometer	sedulously
escarpment	conical	massive
fallibility	oscillations	visage
gesticulate	eminence	maligned
precipitous		

FLIGHT TO THE SOUTH POLE

1   Thanksgiving Day, November 28th, brought what we wanted. At noon the Geological Party radioed a final weather report: "Unchanged. Perfect visibility. No clouds anywhere." Harrison finished with his balloon runs, Haines with his weather charts. The sky was still somewhat overcast, and the surface wind from the east southeast. Haines came into the library, his face grave. Together we went out for a walk and a last look at the weather. What he said exactly I have forgotten, but it was in effect: "If you don't go now, you may never have another chance as good as this." And that was that.

2   The mechanics, Bubier, Roth and Demas, went over the plane for the last time, testing everything with scrupulous care. A line of men passed five-gallon cans of gasoline to several men standing on the wing, who poured them into the wing tanks. Another line fed the stream of gear which flowed into the plane. Black weighed each thing before passing it on to McKinley and June, who were stowing the stuff in the cabin. Hanson went over the radio equipment.

With de Ganahl I made a careful check of the sextant and the watches and chronometers, which were among the last things put aboard. For days de Ganahl and I had nursed the chronometers, checking them against the time tick broadcast every night from the United States. We knew their exact loss or gain.

3   The total weight was approximately 15,000 pounds.

4   Haines came up with a final report on the weather. "A twenty-mile wind from the south at 2,000 feet." I went into my office and picked up a flag weighted with a stone from Floyd Bennett's grave. It seemed fitting that something connected with the spirit of this noble friend, who stood with me over the North Pole, on May 9th, 1926, should rest as long as stone endures at the bottom of the world.

5   There were handshakes all around, and at 3:29 o'clock we were off. The skis were in the air after a run of 30 seconds—an excellent take-off. A calm expectation took hold of my mind.

6   Had you been there to glance over the cabin of this modern machine which has so revolutionized polar travel, I think you would have been impressed most of all—perhaps first of all—with the profusion of gear in the cabin. There was a small sledge, rolled masses of sleeping bags, bulky food sacks, two pressure gasoline stoves, rows of cans of gasoline packed about the main tank forward, funnels for draining gasoline and oil from the engines, bundles of clothing, tents and so on *ad infinitum.* There was scarcely room in which to move.

7   June had his radio in the after bulkhead on the port side. From time to time he flashed reports on our progress to the base. From the ear phones strapped to his helmet ran long cords so that he might move freely about the cabin without being obliged to take them off. His duties were varied and important. He had to attend to the motion picture camera, the radio and the complicated valves of the six gasoline tanks. Every now and then he relieved Balchen at the wheel, or helped him to follow the elusive trail.

8   McKinley had his mapping camera ready for action either on port or starboard side. It was for him and the camera he so sedulously served that the flight was made. The mapping of the corridor between Little America and the South Pole was one of the major objectives of the expedition.

9   Balchen was forward, bulking large in the narrow compartment, his massive hands on the wheel, now appraising the engines with a critical eye, now the dozen flickering fingers on the dials on the instrument board. Balchen was in his element. His calm, fine face bespoke his confidence and sureness. He was anticipating the struggle at the "Hump" almost with eagerness.

10 It was quite warm forward, behind the engines. But a cold wind swept through the cabin, making one thankful for heavy clothes. When the skies cleared, a golden light poured into the cabin. The sound of the engines and propellers filled it. One had to shout to make oneself heard. From the navigation table aft, where my charts were spread out, a trolley ran to the control cabin. Over it I shot to Balchen the necessary messages and courses; he would turn and smile his understanding.

11 That, briefly, is the picture, and a startling one it makes in contrast with that of Amundsen's party, which had pressed along this same course eighteen years before. A wing, pistons and flashing propellers had taken the place of runner, dogs and legs. Amundsen was delighted to make 25 miles per day. We had to average 90 miles per hour to accomplish our mission. We had the advantages of swiftness and comfort, but we had as well an enlarged fallibility. A flaw in a piece of steel, a bit of dirt in the fuel lines or carburetor jets, a few hours

of strong head winds, fog or storm—these things, remotely beyond our control, could destroy our carefully laid plans and nullify our most determined efforts.

12 Still, it was not these things that entered our minds. Rather it was the thought of the "Hump," and how we should fare with it.

13 Soon after passing the crevasses we picked up again the vast escarpment to the right. More clearly than before we saw the white-blue streams of many glaciers discharging into the Barrier, and several of the higher snow-clad peaks glistened so brightly in the sun as to seem like volcanoes in eruption.

14 Now the Queen Maud Range loomed ahead. I searched again for the "appearance of land" to the east. Still the rolling Barrier—nothing else.

15 At 8:15 o'clock we had the Geological Party in sight—a cluster of beetles about two dark-topped tents. Balchen dropped overboard the photographs of the Queen Maud Range and the other things we had promised to bring. The parachute canopy to which they were attached fluttered open and fell in gentle oscillations, and we saw two or three figures rush out to catch it. We waved to them, and then prepared for settlement of the issue at the "Hump."

16 Up to this time, the engines had operated continuously at cruising revolutions. Now Balchen opened them full throttle, and the Ford girded its loins for the long, fighting pull over the "Hump." We rose steadily. We were then about 60 miles north of the western portal of Axel Heiberg, and holding our course steadily on meridian 163° 45′ W. with the sun compass.

17 I watched the altimeters, of which there were two in the navigation department. The fingers marched with little jumps across the face of the dial - 3,000 feet, 3,500 4,000 4,500. The Ford had her toes in, and was climbing with a vast, heaving effort.

18 Drawing nearer, we had edged 30° to the west of south, to bring not only Axel Heiberg but also Liv Glacier into view. This was a critical period. I was by no means certain which glacier I should choose for the ascent, I went forward and took a position behind the pilots.

19 The schemes and hopes of the next few minutes were beset by many uncertainties. Which would it be—Axel Heiberg or Liv Glacier?

20 There was this significant difference between flying and sledging: we could not pause long for decision or investigation. Minutes stood for gasoline, and gasoline was precious. The waste of so little as half an hour of fuel in a fruitless experiment might well overturn the mathematical balance on which the success of the flight depended. The execution of the plan hung on the proper choice of the route over the "Hump."

21 Yet, how well, after all, could judgment forecast the ultimate result? There were few facts on which we might base a decision. We knew, for example, from Amundsen's report, that the highest point of the pass of Axel Heiberg Glacier was 10,500 feet. We should know, in a very few minutes, after June had calculated the gasoline consumption, the weight of the plane. From that we could determine, according to the tables we had worked out and which were then before me, the approximate ceiling we should have. We should know, too, whether or not we should be able to complete the flight, other conditions being favorable.

22 These were the known elements. The unknown were burdened with equally important consequences. The structural nature of the head of the pass was of prime importance. We knew from Amundsen's descriptions and from what we could see with our own eyes, that the pass on both

sides was surrounded by towering peaks, much higher than the maximum ceiling of the heavily loaded plane. But whether the pass was wide or narrow; whether it would allow us room to maneuver in case we could not rise above it; whether it would be narrow and running with a torrent of down-pressing wind which would dash a plane, already hovering near its service ceiling, to the glacier floor—these were things, naturally, we could not possibly know until the issue was directly at hand.

23 I stood beside Balchen, carefully studying the looming fortress, still wondering by what means we should attempt to carry it. With a gesture of the hand Balchen pointed to fog vapor rising from the black rock of the foothills which were Nansen's high priests—caused no doubt by the condensation of warm currents of air radiated from the sun-heated rocks. A thin layer of cloud seemed to cap Axel Heiberg's pass, and extended almost to Liv Glacier. But of this we were not certain. Perhaps it was the surface of the snow. If cloud, then our difficulties were already upon us. Even high clouds would be resting on the floor of the uplifted plateau.

24 There was, then a gamble in the decision. Doubtless a flip of the coin would have served as well. In the end, we decided to choose Liv Glacier, the unknown pass to the right which Amundsen had seen far in the distance and named after Dr. Nansen's daughter. It seemed to be broader than Axel Heiberg, and the pass not quite so high.

25 A few minutes after 9 o'clock we passed near the intermediate base, which, of course, we could not see. Our altitude was then about 9,000 feet. At 9:15 o'clock we had the eastern portal on our left, and were ready to tackle the "Hump." We had discussed the "Hump" so often, had anticipated and maligned it so much, that now

that it was in front of us and waiting in the flesh—in rock-ribbed, glacierized reality—it was like meeting an old acquaintance. But we approached it warily and respectfully, climbing steadily all the while with maximum power, to get a better view of its none too friendly visage.

26 June, wholly unaffected by the immediate perplexities, went about his job of getting the plane in fighting trim. He ripped open the last of the fuel cans, and poured the contents into the main tank. The empty tins he dropped overboard, through the trapdoor. Every tin weighed two pounds; and every pound dropped was to our gain. June examined the gauges of the five wing tanks, then measured with a graduated stick the amount of fuel in the main tank. He jotted the figures on a pad, made a few calculations and handed me the results. Consumption had thus far averaged between 55 and 60 gallons per hour. It had taken us longer to reach the mountains than we had expected, owing to head winds. However, the extra fuel taken aboard just before we left had absorbed this loss and we actually had a credit balance. We had, then, enough gasoline to take us to the Pole and back.

27 With that doubt disposed of, we went at the "Hump" confidently.

28 We were still rising, and the engines were pulling wonderfully well. The wind was about abeam, and, according to my calculations, not materially affecting the speed.

29 The glacier floor rose sharply, in a series of ice falls and terraces, some of which were well above the (then) altitude of the plane. These glacial waterfalls, some of which were from 200 to 400 feet high, seemed more beautiful than any precipitous stream I have ever seen. Beautiful yes, but how rudely and with what finality they would deal with steel and duralumin that crashed into them at 100 miles per hour.

30 Now the stream of air pouring down the pass roughened perceptibly. The great wing shivered and teetered as it balanced itself against the changing pressures. The wind from the left flowed against Fisher's steep flanks, and the constant, hammering bumps made footing uncertain in the plane. But McKinley steadily trained his 50-pound camera on the mountains to the left. The uncertainties of load and ceiling were not his concern. His only concern was photographs—photographs over which students and geographers pore in the calm quiet of their studies.

31 The altimeters showed a height of 9,600 feet, but the figure was not necessarily exact. Nevertheless there were indications we were near the service ceiling of the plane.

32 The roughness of the air increased and became so violent that we were forced to swing slightly to the left, in search of calmer air. This brought us over a frightfully crevassed slope which ran up and toward Mount Nansen. We thus escaped the turbulent swirl about Fisher, but the down-surging currents here damped our climb. To the left we had the "blind" mountain glacier of Nansen in full view; and when we looked ahead we saw the plateau—a smooth, level plain of snow between Nansen and Fisher. The pass rose up to meet it.

33 In the center of the pass was a massive outcropping of snow-covered rocks, resembling an island, which protruded above and separated the descending stream of ice. Perhaps it was a peak or the highest eminence of a ridge connecting Fisher and Nansen which had managed through the ages to hold its head above the glacial torrent pouring down from the plateau. But its particular structure or relationship was of small moment then. I watched it only with reference to the climb of the plane; and realized,

with some disgust and more consternation, that the nose of the plane, in spite of the fact that Balchen had steepened the angle of attack, did not rise materially above the outcropping. We were still climbing, but at a rapidly diminishing rate of speed. In the rarefied air the heavy plane responded to the controls with marked sluggishness. There is a vast difference between the plane of 1928 and the plane of 1937.

34 It was an awesome thing, creeping (so it seemed) through the narrow pass, with the black walls of Nansen and Fisher on either side, higher than the level of the wings, and watching the nose of the ship bob up and down across the face of that chunk of rock. It would move up, then slide down. Then move up, and fall off again. For perhaps a minute or two we deferred the decision; but there was no escaping it. If we were to risk a passage through the pass, we needed greater maneuverability than we had at that moment. Once we entered the pass, there would be no retreat. It offered no room for turn. If power was lost momentarily or if the air became excessively rough, we could only go ahead, or down. We had to climb, and there was only one way in which we could climb.

35 June, anticipating the command, already had his hand on the dump valve of the main tank. A pressure of the fingers—that was all that was necessary—and in two minutes 600 gallons of gasoline would gush out. I signaled to wait.

36 Balchen held to the climb almost to the edge of a stall. But it was clear to both of us that he could not hold it long enough. Balchen began to yell and gesticulate, and it was hard to catch the words in the roar of the engines echoing from the cliffs on either side. But the meaning was manifest. "Overboard—overboard—200 pounds!"

37 Which would it be—gasoline or food?

38 If gasoline, I thought, we might as well stop there and turn back. We could never get back to the base from the Pole. If food, the lives of all of us would be jeopardized in the event of a forced landing. Was that fair to McKinley, Balchen and June? It really took only a moment to reach the decision. The Pole, after all, was our objective. I knew the character of the three men. McKinley, in fact, had already hauled one of the food bags to the trapdoor. It weighed 125 pounds.

39 The brown bag was pushed out and fell, spinning, to the glacier. The improvement in the flying qualities of the plane was noticeable. It took another breath and resumed the climb.

40 Now the down-currents over Nansen became stronger. The plane trembled and rose and fell, as if struck bodily. We veered a trifle to the right, searching for helpful rising eddies. Balchen was flying shrewdly. He maintained flight at a sufficient distance below the absolute ceiling of the plane to retain at all times enough maneuverability to make him master of the ship. But he was hard pressed by circumstances; and I realized that, unless the plane was further lightened, the final thrust might bring us perilously close to the end of our reserve.

41 "More," Bernt shouted. "Another bag."

42 McKinley shoved a second bag through the trapdoor, and this time we saw it hit the glacier, and scatter in a soundless explosion. Two hundred and fifty pounds of food— enough to feed four men for a month—lay strewn on the barren ice.

43 The sacrifice swung the scales. The plane literally rose with a jump; the engines dug in, and we soon showed a gain in altitude of from 300 to 400 feet. It was what we wanted. We should clear the pass with about 500 feet to spare. Balchen gave a shout of joy. It was just as well. We could dump no more food. There was nothing left to dump except McKinley's camera. I am sure that, had he been asked to put it overboard, he would have done so instantly; and I am equally sure he would have followed the precious instrument with his own body.

44 The next few minutes dragged. We moved at a speed of 77 nautical miles per hour through the pass, with the black walls of Nansen on our left. The wing gradually lifted above them. The floor of the plateau stretched in a white immensity to the south. We were over the dreaded "Hump" at last. The Pole lay dead ahead over the horizon, less than 300 miles away. It was then about 9:45 o'clock (I did not note the exact time. There were other things to think about).

45 Gaining the plateau, we studied the situation a moment and then shifted course to the southward. Nansen's enormous towering ridge, lipped by the plateau, shoved its heavily broken sides into the sky. A whole chain of mountains began to parade across the eastern horizon. How high they are I cannot say, but surely some of them must be around 14,000 feet, to stand so boldly above the rim of the 10,000 foot plateau. Peak on peak, ridge on ridge, draped in snow garments which brilliantly reflected the sun, they extended in a solid array to the southeast. But can one really say they ran in that direction? The lines of direction are so bent in this region that 150 miles farther on, even were they to continue in the same general straight line, they must run north of east. This is what happens near the Pole.

46 We laid our line of flight on the 171st meridian.

47 Our altitude was then between 10,500 and 11,000 feet. We were "riding" the engines, conscious of the fact that if one should fail we must come down. Once the starboard engine did sputter a bit, and Balchen nosed

down while June rushed to the fuel valves. But it was nothing; to conserve fuel, Balchen had "leaned" the mixture too much. A quick adjustment corrected the fault, and in a moment the engine took up its steady rhythm. Moments like this one make a pioneering flight anything but dull; one moment everything is lovely, and the next is full of forebodings.

48 From time to time June "spelled" Balchen at the controls; and Balchen would walk back to the cabin, flexing his cramped muscles. There was little thought of food in any of us—a beef sandwich, stiff as a board from frost, and tea and coffee from a thermos bottle. It was difficult to believe that two decades or so before the most resolute men who had ever attempted to carry a remote objective, Scott and Shackleton, had plodded over this same plateau, a few miles each day, with hunger, fierce, unrelenting hunger, stalking them every step of the way.

49 Between 11:30 and 12:30 o'clock the mountains to the eastward began to disappear, dropping imperceptibly out of view, one after another. Not long after 12:30 o'clock the whole range had retreated from vision, and the plateau met the horizon in an indefinite line. The mountains to the right had long since disappeared.

50 The air finally turned smooth. At 12:38 o'clock I shot the sun. It hung, a ball of fire, just beyond *south* to the east, 21° above the horizon. So it was quite low, and we stared it in the eye. The sight gave me an approximate line of latitude, which placed us very near our position as calculated by dead reckoning. That dead reckoning and astronomy should check so closely was very encouraging. The position line placed us at Lat. 89° 4½′ S., or 55½ miles from the Pole. A short time later we reached an altitude of 11,000 feet. According to Amundsen's records, the plateau, which had risen to 10,300 feet, descended here to 9,600 feet.

We were, therefore, about 1,400 feet above the plateau.

51 So the Pole was actually in sight. But I could not yet spare it so much as a glance. Chronometers, drift indicators, and compasses are hard task-masters.

52 Relieved by June, Balchen came aft and reported that visibility was not as good as it had been. Clouds were gathering on the horizon off the port bow; and a storm, Balchen thought, was in the air. A storm was the last thing we wanted to meet on the plateau on the way back. It would be difficult enough to pass the Queen Maud Range in bright sunlight; in thick weather it would be suicidal. Conditions, however, were merely unpromising: not really bad, simply not good. If worse came to worst, we decided we could out-race the clouds to the mountains.

53 At six minutes after one o'clock, a sight of the sun put us a few miles ahead of our dead reckoning position. We were quite close now. At 1:14 o'clock, Greenwich civil time, our calculations showed that we were at the Pole.

54 I opened the trapdoor and dropped over the calculated position of the Pole the small flag which was weighted with the stone from Bennett's grave. Stone and flag plunged down together. The flag had been advanced 1,500 miles farther south than it had ever been advanced by any American or American expedition.

55 For a few seconds we stood over the spot where Amundsen had stood, December 14th, 1911; and where Scott had also stood, thirty-four days later, reading the note which Amundsen had left for him. In their honor, the flags of their countries were again carried over the Pole. There was nothing now to mark that scene: only a white desolation and solitude disturbed by the sound of our engines. The Pole lay in

the center of a limitless plain. To the right, which is to say to the eastward, the horizon was covered with clouds. If mountains lay there, as some geologists believe, they were concealed and we had no hint of them.

56 And that, in brief, is all there is to tell about the South Pole. One gets there, and that is about all there is for the telling. It is the effort to get there that counts.

• • • •

Sunday, Dec. 1

57 ... Well, it's done. We have seen the Pole. McKinley, Balchen and June have delivered the goods. They took the Pole in their stride, neatly, expeditiously, and undismayed. If I had searched the world I doubt if I could have found a better team. Theirs was the actual doing. But there is not a man in this camp who did not assist in the preparation for the flight. Whatever merit accrues to the accomplishment must be shared with them.[2]

[2] Rear Admiral Richard E. Byrd, "Flight to the South Pole." From An American Reader, ed. Burton Rascoe. New York: G.P. Putnam's Sons Copyright © 1938. Excerpt obtained from "Little America," by Rear Admiral Richard E. Byrd. *Used by permission of G.P. Putnam's Sons.

✎ **Answer the following questions about the story.**

3.21 What day and date did this autobiography begin? _____

_____

3.22 What is the setting throughout the narrative? _____

_____

3.23 What fills the inside of the cabin? _____

_____

3.24 In Paragraph 9 what does Byrd tell the reader about Balchen? _____

_____

3.25 Why is the description or setting in Paragraph 10 important later at the "Hump"?

_____

3.26 After Paragraph 22 how does the setting increase the suspense in this narrative?

_____

3.27 What type of men are these explorers? _____

_____

3.28 In Paragraph 21 what determined which pass they would take? _____

_____

3.29 In Paragraph 26 Admiral Byrd gives a personal glimpse of June. What is he like?

_____

_____

3.30 What does Byrd say about McKinley's character in Paragraphs 30 and 43?

_____

_____

3.31 What are three incidents described in Paragraphs 32 through 42 that affect Byrd and his

companions? _____

_____

3.32 What does Paragraph 38 reveal about Byrd? _____

_____

3.33 What is the turning point in the action? (Give paragraph number also.)

_____

_____

3.34 What do the two incidents described in Paragraphs 47 and 48 tell you about Byrd's

personal character? _____

_____

3.35 What do you feel is the theme of this autobiography? _____

_____

Write the letter of the definition for each of the vocabulary words.

3.36 _____ scrupulous   a. with risk

3.37 _____ chronometer   b. prominence

3.38 _____ massive   c. appearance

3.39 _____ gesticulate   d. slandered

3.40 _____ profusion   e. careful

3.41 _____ sedulously   f. abundance

3.42 _____ fallibility   g. fluctuations

3.43 _____ eminence   h. long cliff

3.44 _____ perilously   i. huge

3.45 _____ escarpment   j. dismay

3.46 _____ oscillations   k. diligently

3.47 _____ maligned   l. timepiece

3.48 _____ consternation   m. gesture

3.49 _____ conical   n. the quality of tending to fail

3.50 _____ visage   o. cone-shaped

3.51 _____ precipitous   p. steep

Complete this activity.

3.52 Write a 250- to 500-word autobiography.

TEACHER CHECK _____ _____
                            initials   date

SPELLING

The spelling list for this section is made up of vocabulary words from the text and the autobiographies.

Spelling Words-3		
narrative	conical	sedulously
irrelevant	consternation	eminence
elongated	reluctantly	fallibility
scrupulous	prominent	controversies
census	galvanized	cistern
subsistence	oscillations	vaguely
precipitous	maligned	rural
visage	profusion	

Write a sentence with each of the following words.

3.53 narrative _____

_____

3.54 irrelevant _____

_____

3.55 scrupulous _____

_____

3.56 precipitous _____

_____

3.57 conical _____

_____

3.58 profusion _____

_____

3.59 fallibility _____

_____

3.60 visage _____

_____

 **Complete this activity.**

3.61   This puzzle contains some of your spelling words.

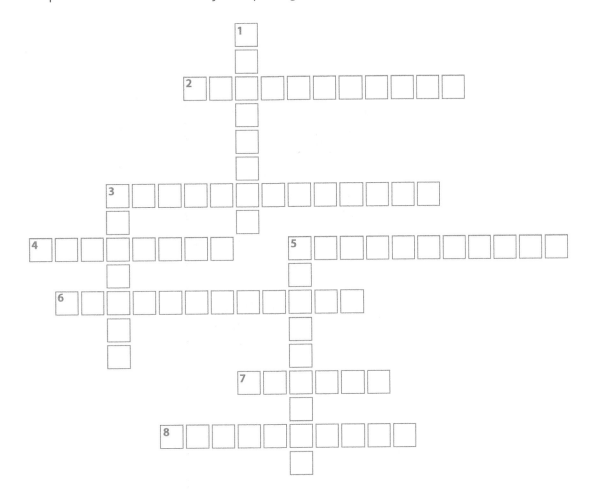

Across

2. The quality of tending to fail

3. Dismay

4. Prominence

5. Extremely steep

6. Fluctuations

7. Appearance

8. Diligently

Down

1. Slandered

3. Cone-shaped

5. Abundance

ABC **Ask your teacher to give you a practice spelling test of Spelling Words-3.** Restudy the words you missed.

Before you take this last Self Test, you may want to do one or more of these self checks.

1. _____ Read the objectives. See if you can do them.
2. _____ Restudy the material related to any objectives that you cannot do.
3. _____ Use the **SQ3R** study procedure to review the material:
   a. **S**can the sections.
   b. **Q**uestion yourself.
   c. **R**ead to answer your questions.
   d. **R**ecite the answers to yourself.
   e. **R**eview areas you did not understand.
4. _____ Review all vocabulary, activities, and Self Tests, writing a correct answer for every wrong answer.

SELF TEST 3

Write the letter of the correct answer (each answer, 2 points).

3.01 _____ Mercian

3.02 _____ Beowulf

3.03 _____ elegy

3.04 _____ Chaucer

3.05 _____ Bede

3.06 _____ Alfred

3.07 _____ Danelaw

3.08 _____ *Comitatus*

3.09 _____ Romans

3.010 _____ Sutton Hoo

a. an Anglo-Saxon king

b. a site of a ship burial

c. Anglo-Saxon dialect

d. occupied England in 55 B.C.

e. hero of an epic

f. fourteenth-century writer

g. Anglo-Saxon group formed by leader and men

h. poem dealing with serious thoughts

i. area of England given to the Danes

j. Anglo-Saxon scholar

k. Celtic hero

Write the letter of the correct answer. Each sentence will demonstrate the proper use of one or more elements (each answer, 2 points).

3.011 _____ Joe and his dad watched the huge fish on the end of the line.
a. using a common verb with compound subject
b. a series using the same verb
c. a compound sentence
d. a relative clause

3.012 _____ Both New York City and Chicago are fascinating places to visit.
a. a pair of conjunctives
c. a correlative pair
b. a combination of clauses
d. an appositive

3.013 _____ I took swimming lessons at church camp, although I already know how to swim.
a. a condition relationship expressed by the conjunction
b. a subordinate conjunction
c. an adverb clause
d. a, b, and c

3.014 _____ Remembering the cake, Heather's mom dashed back into her kitchen.
a. a participial phrase
b. a prepositional phrase
c. an appositive phrase
d. a correlative conjunction

3.015 _____ Karen finally found her new blue coat, which had been left on the bench.
  a. conjunctive adverb
  b. appositive
  c. a conditional relationship
  d. adjective clause

Write the letter of the correct answer (each answer, 2 points).

3.016 The time an autobiography was written is important because _____ .
  a. it helps the reader to identify with the author
  b. the political and social conditions may have affected the author
  c. the balance of location and time helps reveal the theme
  d. the history of the book gives unity to the personal glimpses

3.017 The turning point helps the reader _____ .
  a. to assess the effect significant moments had on the author's life
  b. to relate the incidents to one's personal life
  c. to evaluate the lesson to be learned
  d. to place the story in time and history

3.018 The theme of the autobiography is important to the reader because it _____ .
  a. determines the success of the author
  b. relates a significant summary of the author's intent
  c. may have significance to their personal life
  d. forces the reader to evaluate his own life

3.019 In which of these autobiographies would the reader most likely have to be cautious of the theme? _____
  a. _The Sound of Music_ by Maria Von Trapp
  b. _Mein Kampf_ by Adolf Hitler
  c. _The Hiding Place_ by Corrie ten Boom
  d. _Tortured for Christ_ by Richard Wurmbrand

3.020 A reader carefully evaluates the theme of a book _____ .
  a. because it may disagree with the popular views of life
  b. because it may raise unanswerable questions in the reader's mind
  c. because it may not encourage the reader to improve themself
  d. because it may present values and ideals directly opposed to those of the reader

Answer true or false (each answer, 1 point).

3.021 _____ Jesse Stuart was only sixteen years old when he began teaching school.

3.022 _____ Stuart wanted to teach in the city but had to accept the country school since he was a beginning teacher.

3.023 _____ John Conway was the large troublemaker Stuart had to stand up to.

3.024 _____ The children wore tattered clothing and poorly fitting shoes.

3.025 _____ Stuart taught thirty-five students in an old-fashioned one-room schoolhouse.

Complete these sentences (each answer, 3 points).

3.026 In an autobiography describing a voyage in a spacecraft, the essential element would
probably be the _____ .

3.027 If an author mentions a world leader or a famous event, the reader will be able to
determine the _____ of the story.

3.028 In an autobiography if an author mentions a close friend, the important element here
would be _____ .

3.029 An author mentioning a significant occurrence that deeply affected them is revealing
a _____ in their life and study.

3.030 The author's intent and how they view their life is an element called _____ .

48
/60   **SCORE** _____   **TEACHER** _____ _____
                                                                initials   date

ABC **Take your spelling test of Spelling Words-3.**

Before taking the LIFEPAC Test, you may want to do one or more of these self checks.

1. _____ Read the objectives. See if you can do them.
2. _____ Restudy the material related to any objectives that you cannot do.
3. _____ Use the **SQ3R** study procedure to review the material.
4. _____ Review activities, Self Tests, and LIFEPAC vocabulary words.
5. _____ Restudy areas of weakness indicated by the last Self Test.
6. _____ Review all spelling words in this LIFEPAC.